Date Due

COSMIC RADIATION

COSMIC RADIATION

FIFTEEN LECTURES
EDITED BY

W. HEISENBERG

TRANSLATED BY

T. H. JOHNSON

PUBLISHED AND DISTRIBUTED IN THE PUBLIC INTEREST BY
AUTHORITY OF THE U. S. ALIEN PROPERTY CUSTODIAN
UNDER LICENSE NO. A-1185

DOVER PUBLICATIONS
NEW YORK
1946

PRINTED IN THE UNITED STATES OF AMERICA
BY THE WILLIAM BYRD PRESS, INC.
RICHMOND, VIRGINIA

FOREWORD TO THE AMERICAN EDITION

This series of symposia on cosmic ray problems was published in Berlin in 1943 by Springer-Verlag in commemoration of the 75th birthday of Arnold Sommerfeld. Although written by several authors the articles are well integrated with numerous cross references and a self consistent notation, and they present a general view of some of the recent accomplishments and outstanding problems in a branch of physics which is destined to attract many workers in the next few years.

On the very day which the book was intended to commemorate, and before many copies had been distributed, bombs fell on Berlin destroying the plates and the entire stock of printed volumes. In order to make the material available to American physicists the present translation has been prepared. Acknowledgement is due to Professor S. Goudsmit who kindly loaned me his copy of the German text.

T. H. JOHNSON

FOREWORD TO THE GERMAN EDITION

The investigations on cosmic radiation have been sharply curtailed by the misfortunes of the times. On the one hand, in most physical laboratories they have taken second place with respect to other problems, and, on the other hand, the failure of the usual channels of communication makes it difficult to obtain information as to the results obtained in other countries. Finally, comprehensive reports have not appeared in Germany during war time since the physicists employed in war research have not found the time for comprehensive work of this kind. Because of the importance of this branch of physics, it therefore seemed appropriate to have this series of symposia bound together and published in book form as a survey of the present state of the cosmic ray investigation.

These symposia were held in the years 1941 and 1942 in the Kaiser Wilhelm-Institut for Physics; they give an insight into the state of certain individual questions as far as is possible in view of the fact that the American literature was available only up to the summer of 1941. In small measure they contain some results which have not been published elsewhere. I refer to the investigations of Molière on the large showers, the calculations of Flügge on the neutron distribution in the atmosphere, and a simplified cascade theory which originated from some lectures which I gave in the summer of 1939 in Leipzig and at Purdue University, Lafayette (USA).

Taken together, these contributions should give a unified, representative picture of our knowledge of cosmic radiation at about the end of the year 1941. This picture is not very satisfactory. The genetics of the various kinds of rays is still insufficiently clear, and the mechanism of their transformations is precisely known only in the case of electrons and light quanta. One can only hope, therefore, that the picture presented here will be replaced as soon as possible by one which is clearer and more nearly correct.

It was the wish of all contributors to dedicate this book to Arnold Sommerfeld on the occasion of his 75th birthday. Our thanks to the teacher of atomic physics in Germany should be best expressed by the fact that the scientific method which Sommerfeld began in his Munich school has been continued by the younger teachers and has borne fruit.

For their trouble in writing and correcting the papers I must thank all of my associates and also, especially, the publisher, who willingly supported the publication of the papers and successfully overcame all of the practical difficulties.

Berlin-Dahlem

June 2, 1943   W. HEISENBERG

CONTENTS

Introduction

Cascades

Mesons

Nuclear Particles

Geomagnetic Effects

CONTENTS

Introduction

Cascades

Mesons

Nuclear Particles

Geomagnetic Effects

INTRODUCTION

1. REVIEW OF THE PRESENT STATE OF OUR KNOWLEDGE OF COSMIC RADIATION

By W. HEISENBERG, Berlin-Dahlem

Since the investigations by Hess (H 11) and Kolhörster (K 3), it has been recognized that a radiation incident upon the earth from external space incites in the atmosphere various secondary phenomena, which reveal themselves by setting up a general ionization caused by various kinds of elementary particles (electrons, light quanta, mesons, protons, neutrons). As a result, this radiation becomes weaker and weaker as it penetrates deeper into the atmosphere or the earth, until at an equivalent depth of about 1000 m. of water it has practically vanished. (Cf. also the summarizing articles of Miehlnickel (M 3a), Steinke (S 18a), Steinmaurer (S 18b), and in Rev. Mod. Phys. 11, 122, 1939). To classify these effects of the so-called ultra-, höhen- or cosmic radiation it has been customary for some time to divide the cosmic rays in the atmosphere into components. The various components differ as regards the kind of particles and their origin. At the present state of our knowledge one can distinguish four components. The existence of a fifth component, which has been noticed at very great depths, is also probable, according to a few investigations. The four components may be described in the following manner.

1. **The soft radiation (cascade radiation).** It consists of electrons, positrons, and light quanta, which undergo transformations from one to another in accordance with the laws of the cascade theory; it represents the principal part of the cosmic radiation from a height of about 7 km. on up to very great heights. The well known maximum of ionization at about 16 to 20 km. is also probably produced by this electron radiation. At sea level the intensity of this component has already shrunk to a very small fraction of the initial intensity.

2. **The penetrating radiation.** This consists of mesons which are produced in the atmosphere by another radiation (most probably protons or light quanta). Its intensity, according to all measurements thus far made, increases continuously to the greatest heights without passing through a maximum, although a maximum must definitely occur somewhere since the mesons as radioactive particles cannot come to the earth from external space. Perhaps there are different kinds of mesons, distinguished by different values of spin moment and mean life time and making

up the penetrating component with different relative intensities at different heights. This component decreases with increasing depth much more slowly than the soft component and can be detected down to depths of 400 m. of water and more.

3. The soft secondary radiation of the mesons. This consists of electrons, positrons, and light quanta which are formed by the mesons through collision processes and through radioactive decay. In general, it is in equilibrium with the meson component but falls off with increasing depth somewhat more slowly than the meson intensity, a fact which is to be associated with the increasing hardness of the meson radiation.

4. The proton and neutron radiation. Its intensity runs parallel to that of the soft component up to great heights; this fact indicates that, at least in the lower atmospheric layers, the proton-neutron component is formed to a preponderant degree by the soft component. Moreover, strong arguments support the view that protons are incident upon the earth from external space, perhaps even representing the principal part of the primary radiation, and that, at very great heights, the proton component is, for the most part, a primary radiation, which there excites the meson components and the cascade radiation. The intensity of the neutrons is much greater than that of the protons, a fact which is apparently associated with the much greater range of the neutrons.

In what follows, the most important properties which have, thus far, been discovered of the four components will be summarized in a short review.

1. Cascade Radiation

If one extrapolates the spectrum of the soft component from the heights at which measurements have been made up to the top of the atmosphere— the multiplication and the absorption of this component is completely governed by the cascade theory—one obtains a simple spectrum. For a long time this was regarded as the primary spectrum of the cosmic radiation. Thus if one assumes that—above an energy of about 3 to $4 \cdot 10^9 \mathrm{eV}$— a number $F(E)$ of electrons of energy greater than E, given by

$$F(E) \approx 0.05 \cdot \left(\frac{10^{10}\mathrm{eV}}{E}\right)^{1.8} (\sec^{-1}\mathrm{cm}^{-2}), \qquad (1)$$

is incident upon the earth, one can explain the variation of the soft component with height, the maximum of the ionization, and the latitude effect —the magnetic field of the earth cuts the spectrum (1) off at a given energy, depending upon the magnetic latitude. The large Hoffman bursts and the frequency of large showers are also explained nearly correctly.

According to this explanation the primary spectrum (1) should contain no electrons of energy below a given limit determined by the latitude, which in our latitude, as an example, is at about $5 \cdot 10^9$eV. These electrons are then multiplied from the top of the atmosphere on down according to the cascade theory, thus producing the maximum of ionization; the whole spectrum is absorbed exponentially but continues to keep its form (1).

In northern latitudes the maximum is relatively high and steep, since the primary spectrum consists of many particles of relatively low energy; at the equator it is appreciably lower since it is produced by a relatively few high energy particles. (cf. the well known measurements of Millikan, Bowen, and Neher, (B 32, 33, 34) and Fig. 1). At sea level the soft com-

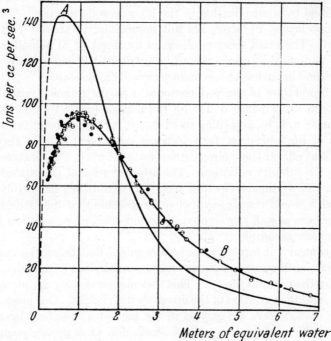

Fig. 1. Intensity of the cosmic radiation as a function of the thickness of the air layer passed through, according to Bowen, Millikan and Neher. Curve *B*: Intensity in Madras (3° north magnetic latitude).
Curve *A*: Difference of intensities in Fort Sam Houston (38.5° north latitude) and Madras.

ponent is already reduced to a small fraction of the primary intensity, constituting only about 5 to 10% of the total intensity observed there.

The soft rays always start cascades when incident upon matter with great energy. Thus, on the one hand, large showers are formed in the atmosphere, and, on the other, the showers observed by Rossi (R 5) and the Hoffman (H 12) bursts are produced in solid matter. The air showers which stem from very energetic electrons reach into greater depths; they have been observed by Auger (A 10), Kolhörster (K 4, 5), and their associates. They fill a cylindrical volume of some 50 m. radius with electrons, the density and the height of the cylinder depending upon the primary energy. The observed showers arise in part from electrons of more than 10^{15}eV. The frequency of these showers, therefore, offers a possibility of testing the spectrum (1) to very high energies, and the results confirm the value 1.8 of the exponent in (1). According to Euler these measurements give as exponent a value 1.8 ± 0.17.

The Hoffman bursts in the ionization chambers behind thin layers of solid matter are likewise to be regarded as an effect of air showers, which are intensified by multiplication in the layer of solid matter. The bursts behind thick layers, however, are not immediately traceable to the soft component. The small showers observed by Rossi (R 5) behind layers of matter of various thicknesses are to be attributed in part to the cascade component and in part to the secondary rays of the mesons.

The interpretation of the soft component as the primary radiation has recently been thrown into doubt by the measurements by Schein, Jesse, and Wollan (S 4, 5, 6), according to whom, at very great heights above the maximum of the ionization, fast electrons are present only in very small numbers, if at all. If these observations are confirmed, the soft component cannot be the primary radiation. The interpretation of the latitude effect on the basis of a primary electron spectrum would then have to be abandoned, and it would remain somewhat remarkable that the latitude effect could have been so well represented. Happily, this representation has not been altogether accurate.

On the contrary, it must always be recognized that below the maximum of the ionization the soft component has essentially the form which follows from (1) by the cascade theory. This is demonstrated by the air showers, the bursts, and the variation of the intensity with height. One must assume that these cascade rays are excited in the highest atmosphere by another component—for example, by collision-radiation of a proton component, or by collision-radiation and radioactive decay of a meson radiation, or by explosive processes, which stem from energetic protons and lead to the production of many mesons and many light quanta and electrons. As to the details of these processes, nothing is yet known.

Since in all of these processes a part of the primary energy is not transformed in the highest atmosphere into cascade radiation, the primary radiation must contain more energy than is given by the spectrum(1). Thus the latitude effect at the maximum of the ionization, if this is produced by the soft radiation, must be less than that given by the present theory. This presents a difficulty which raises the question whether the maximum of the ionization is really produced by electrons, and, if this is the case, through what processes do these electrons come into being.

2. The Meson Component

The mesons originate in the atmosphere; they do not come to the earth from external space. This follows from the radioactive instability of the meson, which has been established by a series of experiments. Johnson (J 9) has concluded from the east-west effect of the penetrating component and from the excess of positive rays among the primaries which give rise to mesons that most mesons originate from a primary proton component. An intense proton component of this nature has not yet been observed, and one must, therefore, assume that the energetic protons are rapidly absorbed in the highest layers of the atmosphere. However, the excitation of mesons has been observed even in deeper layers of the atmosphere below 7 km. According to the observations, this meson excitation runs parallel to the intensity of the soft component, and it is, therefore, probable that the soft component is responsible for it. In addition, in this process slow mesons seem to be produced preferentially (cf. the measurements of Schein, Wollan, and Groetzinger (S 8) and Hertzog and Bostick (H 8, 9)). One, therefore, thinks of processes, analogous to the usual pair production, by which a light quantum forms a meson pair at a nucleus. Energetic light quanta appear to be able to release explosive processes, by which, under some circumstances, many mesons are created at once. Processes of this kind have been observed by Fussell (F 7), Powell (P 6), Wollan (W 16), and Daudin (D 1) in the Wilson chamber, and the observations of Santos, Pompeja, and Wataghin (W 2) and of Jánossy and Ingleby (J 3) on the penetrating showers indicate the same thing.

The meson component is weakened on its path through the atmosphere, on the one hand, by the well known ionizing collisions and, on the other hand, by radioactive decay of the meson. The collisions can be treated by the well known formula of Bethe (B 10) and Bloch (B 26); Fermi (F 1) has recently shown that these formulas should be improved in their application to solid matter, and that the number of collisions per gm./cm.^{2} in dense matter is somewhat less than in matter of low density. Furthermore, Kemmer (K 1) has deduced from the Yukawa theory that the transfer of large amounts of energy by mesons of high energy can take place with an effective collision cross section which is much larger than the corresponding cross section for the collision of two electrons. Through such collisions the absorption of energetic mesons is increased. The radioactive decay of mesons takes place, according to the Yukawa theory, in such a manner that the meson breaks up into an electron and a neutrino, each of which, in the rest system of the meson, receives about half of the mass of the meson or about 40 to 50 MeV in the form of kinetic energy. According to the available experimental evidence, the mean decay period for mesons, at sea level is about 1.5 to 2.5 · 10^{-6} sec. when measured in the rest system of the meson, and it increases for rapidly moving mesons, according to time dilatation of the relativity theory, in the ratio of the energy to the rest energy. This can be demonstrated experimentally from the absorption of mesons in air, from the resulting temperature and barometer effects, from the form of the spectrum in the low energy region, and from the number of decay electrons. The radioactive decay has been directly demonstrated by photographs in the Wilson chamber by Williams (W 12).

The spectrum of mesons at their point of origin in the high atmosphere seems to follow quite well a law of the form

$$G(E) = \text{const } E^{-\gamma} \tag{2}$$

[$G(E)$ = number of mesons of energy exceeding E] in which the exponent γ, within the limits of precision of the measurements, is of the same magnitude as that for the soft component ($\gamma \sim 1.8$). This follows, in the first place, from the drop of meson intensity with depth T which obeys a $T^{-\gamma}$ law in absorbing layers up to 300 m. of water and, in the second place, from the energy distribution of the cascade bursts excited by mesons. However, at depths below 300 m. of water the absorption becomes stronger; yet this does not arise from any deviation from the $E^{-\gamma}$ law but rather from the added absorption deduced by Kemmer. This comes into effect because the energetic mesons can transfer an appreciable part of their energy to an electron with a collision cross section which is independent of the energy; perhaps there are other additional secondary processes. (cf. also the work of Oppenheimer, Snyder, and Serber (O 2) and Lyons (L 12)).

The similarity of spectra (1) and (2) suggests a genetic relation between the two spectra. It is probable either that the meson component originates from the soft component, or that the soft component originates from the meson component, or that both components originate from the same primary component. Previously, the first assumption has been taken as the most probable. If the observations by Schein, Jesse, and Wollan (S 4, 5, 6), which indicate a secondary character of the soft component, are confirmed, then the second or third assumption would be the more probable.

An interesting possibility for the interpretation of these results has been afforded by various theoretical investigations by Oppenheimer, Snyder, and Serber (O 2), Moeller and Rosenfeld (M 5) and Rosental (R 11); the theory of nuclear forces requires the existence of mesons of spin 1, or of two kinds of mesons of spin 1 and of spin 0. From the frequency of meson-excited cascade showers, Oppenheimer has concluded that the mesons observed at sea level probably have spin 0. One can, therefore, assume that in the high atmosphere the two kinds of mesons of spin 0 and spin 1 are generated by the proton component with comparable probability, and that the mesons of spin 1 have a very short life, of the order of 10^{-8} sec., as required by the Yukawa theory, while the mesons of spin 0 have the longer life observed. The mesons of spin 1 are, therefore, absorbed in the highest atmosphere, and their energy is transformed predominantly into cascade rays—through radiation by the energetic mesons and by the decay of the low energy mesons—and only mesons of spin 0 can penetrate to the deeper atmospheric layers. The future alone can judge whether this interpretation can serve as a working hypothesis. Meanwhile, the genetics of the various components of the cosmic radiation is very uncertain.

3. The Soft Secondary Radiation of the Mesons

This radiation comprises two components: the electrons (and their cascades) which have received a high energy from a meson collision (Bhabha (B 19)), and those which result from meson decay (Euler (E 4)). Theoretically, for both components, the form of the spectrum is represented approximately by

$$H(E) = \text{const } E^{-2 \cdot 8}. \qquad (3)$$

Both spectra, therefore, behave alike and fall off by about one power faster than the meson or the soft component. The Kemmer knock-on process likewise gives a weak additional spectrum of the form $E^{-1 \cdot 8}$.

The soft secondary radiation is, in general, already in equilibrium with the meson radiation after a relatively thin layer of matter, of the order of the radiation unit of the cascade theory, has been traversed. The relative number of knock-on electrons in equilibrium with the meson component is greater at great depths than at sea level since the mean energy of the mesons increases with depth. In air at sea level the total ionizing radiation is made up of 75 to 80% mesons, about 5% knock-on electrons, 10 to 15% decay electrons, and from 5 to 10% soft primary rays. Behind thick layers of dense matter practically all of the contribution of the decay electrons disappears since those formed in the air are absorbed, but in the relatively short distances in dense matter no new ones can be formed. Theoretically, the number of knock-on electrons in equilibrium in matter of high atomic number should be greater than in substances of low atomic number.

Since the soft secondary rays of the mesons behave like the soft primary rays, they also produce showers and bursts. At sea level, however, practically all of the large showers or bursts are to be ascribed to the soft primary rays, since the spectrum of the soft secondary rays falls off much faster and, therefore, contains fewer energetic electrons than the primary spectrum. It is different behind thick layers of dense matter. Here the primary spectrum can no longer play a rôle, and the bursts still observed there are to be attributed, according to Oppenheimer, Snyder, and Serber (O 2), to such processes as that investigated by Kemmer (K 1). The frequency of the observed bursts falls qualitatively in line with this assumption. Moreover, the collision processes assumed here are of the kind in which the radiation forces of the Yukawa theory must play a decisive rôle, and the applicability of the usual form of the quantum theory is very problematical. One must, therefore, reckon with the possibility that in a burst a number of mesons are excited simultaneously, as is plausible when a strong Yukawa radiation is emitted. One might then be able to cope with the truly explosive showers, which seem to be of common occurrence as already demonstrated not only by the Wilson photographs of Fussell (F 7), Powell (P 6), Wollan (W 16) and Daudin (D 1) but also by the coincidence measurements of Pompeja, Santos, and Wataghin (W 2) and of Jánossy and Ingleby (J 3).

4. The Proton-Neutron Component

Johnson (J 9) has enunciated and given supporting evidence for the hypothesis that the mesons are generated by a primary proton component, and the observations on the secondary character of the soft component suggest that the whole phenomenon of the cosmic radiation is to be attributed to a proton constituted primary radiation from external space. If one adopts this hypothesis—and only future experiments can give the matter final clarification—then he can make the following assumption about the primary proton component: With regard to its energy distribution, the primary proton component is given by a spectrum of the form (1)

$$F(E) = \text{const } E^{-1 \cdot 8} \tag{4}$$

where the constant is certainly greater than that in equation (1). This proton component is transformed in the highest atmosphere into other components, and even at a height of 20 km. most of its energy is already to be found in the soft and in the meson components, (1) and (2) respectively. The form (4) of the spectrum should be sufficient to explain the corresponding form of spectra (1) and (2). This primary proton spectrum is apparently strongly absorbed in the atmosphere since, at the greatest heights where protons have thus far been sought, only a relatively weak proton component has been found. The basis for this strong absorption must be sought in nuclear processes and in radiation by collision. It may also have been established that neutrons are *not* to be considered as primary cosmic rays since, according to the theory of β-decay, they are radioactively unstable. However, the disintegration of neutrons has not yet been proven experimentally.

From the greatest heights down to sea level one finds a relatively weak proton and about a 100 times stronger neutron component. These rays are not directly connected with the primary radiation. Their intensity varies with the height in exact parallel with the intensity of the soft component, according to Fünfer (F 6) and Korff (K 6), and it can, therefore, be regarded, except in the uppermost layers of the atmosphere, as a secondary radiation of the soft component. The number of neutrons is comparable with the electrons of this component; that of the slow protons is smaller by a factor of about 100. Simultaneously with single proton tracks, frequent nuclear disintegrations in which several (up to twelve) nuclear fragments have been thrown out of the nucleus, have been observed on photographic plates exposed at great heights (Blau and Wambacher (B 25), Schopper (S 12)). Here one has to deal, apparently, either with processes by which, perhaps through primary light quanta, energetic protons and neutrons are thrown out of the nucleus, or with secondary processes, which themselves are initiated by fast heavy particles (Bagge (B 1)). It is also natural to associate these processes with the creation of mesons and to assume that an explosive process is set off in the nucleus by a photon in which mesons and heavy particles are simultaneously created and that these, in turn, can summon up other secondary processes in the same nucleus. The assumption that the mesons in the middle atmosphere and the heavy particles are created by the same process, and frequently in the same act, is compatible with the frequency of the nuclear processes and of the various kinds of particles. (Bagge (B 1)). The photographs of Fussell (F 7), as well as basic principles, support the statement that the meson production is, for the most part, tied in with nuclear processes. Yet the experimental evidence now at hand is not sufficiently conclusive to settle this question.

The absorption of the neutron-proton component takes place quite differently for the two kinds of particles. The protons, if they do not have a very high initial energy, are rapidly slowed down by ionization. The neutrons, on the contrary, are absorbed by nuclear processes or, more frequently, they are slowed down by nuclear collisions until finally they are caught as slow neutrons in such nuclei as, for example, N or H.

5. Other Components

The meson component can be followed down to depths of more than 400 m. of water; in the greater depths it becomes weaker relatively fast. But even in 1000 m. depth of water an ionization caused by cosmic rays

can be definitely demonstrated (cf. for example, the investigations of Clay
(C 4) and his associates). Measurements by Barnothy and Forro (B 6)
indicate that here the ionization is produced principally by a soft radiation.
If this is correct, the result can be explained by the assumption that the
cosmic rays are carried to these depths by a new electrically neutral component; as the carrying agent, one can invoke a neutral Yukawa particle or
a Pauli neutrino. However, these questions can be answered only by
further measurements.

CASCADES

2. THE CASCADE THEORY

By W. HEISENBERG[1], Berlin-Dahlem

In passing through matter electrons and positrons excite light quanta; in
their passage through matter light quanta excite electrons and positrons.
In the interplay of these processes the energy of a fast particle divides itself
again and again into a large number of slow particles; a cascade is generated. The multiplication and absorption of the soft component and the
formation of showers and bursts are founded upon this process. The following section will present by deductive reasoning the mathematical
theory of cascade formation. Comparison with experiment is left for later
sections.

1. The Elementary Processes

a) **Radiation-by-collision.** If an electron[2] flies past a charged particle,
it will be deflected from its original direction of flight. With this deflection
there is associated a transfer of energy to the deflecting particle. For
electrons whose velocities differ appreciably from that of light this is the
most important cause of their retardation in passing through matter.
The principal rôle is played by the outer electrons of the atoms, and the
usual result is ionization. This kind of energy loss will be called "ionization" for short.

In the case of very fast electrons another energy-losing process becomes
more important than the ionization; i.e. radiation-by-collision. With the
change of direction of the electron's path there is associated a change of
the electro-magnetic field in the electron's vicinity. Therewith the electron
becomes the starting point of an electromagnetic wave, or, according to
quantum language, there are emitted one or more light quanta. The
probability of this process has been calculated by Sauter (S 1a), and by
Bethe and Heitler (B 16). The effective cross-section dQ for the emission

---

[1]The following text was composed by C. F. v. Weizsäcker after a symposium by W.
Heisenberg and with the use of a derivation by D. Lyons. Extensive calculations by
S. Flügge and G. Molière were also used.

[2]Unless stated to the contrary we will understand by the word *electron* both the
positive and negative particle.

of a light quantum whose energy lies between k and $k + dk$ by an electron of energy E passing by a nucleus of charge Ze is

$$dQ = 4\,\frac{Z^2 e^2}{\hbar c}\left(\frac{e^2}{mc^2}\right)^2\frac{dk}{k}\left\{\left[\frac{4}{3}\left(1-\frac{k}{E}\right)+\left(\frac{k}{E}\right)^2\right]\log\frac{183}{Z^{1/3}} + \text{smaller terms}\right\}. \quad (1)$$

Since the effective cross section is proportional to Z^2, the effect of the atom nucleus must be considered as large compared with that of the orbital electrons, except in the case of the very lightest elements, which are not of particular interest in relation to the cosmic rays. The effect of the orbital electrons comes into the above formula only in the logarithmic term; this term owes its form to the calculation of the external screening of the nuclear field by the method of Thomas and Fermi.

The factor in brackets in (1) has the value 4/3 for $k = 0$, 11/12 for $k = E/2$, and 1 for $K = E$. Only a small error is introduced if it is always written as unity. This approximation will be used in what follows; the error is less than that of other approximations to be made. We obtain then for the number of light quanta in the interval dk, which an electron of energy $E \gg mc^2$ excites by collision along a path interval dx:

$$dn(k) = \frac{dx}{x_0} \cdot \frac{dk}{k}. \quad (2)$$

Here the length x_0, designated as the radiation unit, is defined by

$$\frac{1}{x_0} = 4NZ^2\,\frac{e^2}{\hbar c}\cdot\left(\frac{e^2}{mc^2}\right)^2\log\frac{183}{Z^{1/3}}. \quad (3)$$

N is the number of scattering atomic nuclei per cc. From now on all lengths will be measured in radiation units. If lengths measured in radiation units are designated by the letter l, Equation (2) takes the simple form

$$dn(k) = dl \cdot \frac{dk}{k}. \quad (4)$$

The reciprocal of the radiation unit increases nearly quadratically with the atomic number and linearly with the density of the retarding matter. For lead the radiation unit is 1/2 cm., for air over 300 m. A table for various substances is given in the following chapter by G. Molière (p. 33).

The radiation unit is the distance over which the energy of an electron decreases on the average to $1/e$ of its original value. The mean energy loss per cm. is

$$\frac{dE}{dx} = -\frac{1}{x_0}\int_0^E \frac{dk}{k}\cdot k = -\frac{E}{x_0} \quad (5)$$

and hence

$$E = E_0\, e^{-x/x_0}. \tag{6}$$

One can say: the number of light quanta lying between k and $k + dk$ which are excited along the unit path x_0 is proportional to $1/k$, while the total energy, proportional to $k \cdot 1/k$, is the same for quanta of all energies. That is to say, all energy losses are about equally probable. Since the energy lost per unit path by ionization is practically independent of the primary energy, one understands the dominance of the energy loss through radiation-by-collision for high primary energies.

    b) **Pair formation.** In passing through matter light quanta whose energies are not large compared with mc^2 lose energy by the Compton effect and the photo-electric effect, i.e. by collisions with electrons. The light quanta of the cosmic rays, on the contrary, lose their energy predominantly by the formation of electron pairs. This process bears a certain analogy to radiation-by-collision; according to the Dirac theory of positrons it can be regarded as the inverse of the collision radiation process. In radiating by collision an electron in passing near a nucleus makes a transition from a state of high energy to one of lower energy. In the inverse of this process a light quantum in passing by a nucleus (which is necessary for the process in order to take up the excess momentum resulting from the conservation laws) is absorbed by an electron, which then goes to a state of higher energy. Pair formation comes in then when the absorbing electron is originally in one of the possible negative energy states of the Dirac theory. As long as its energy was negative, this electron belonged to an infinite density of electrons of negative energy and, according to the assumption of Dirac, could not exercise any physical effect. However, if it receives some positive energy, in the first place it becomes real, and, in the second place, the remaining gap in the distribution of electrons of negative energy appears as a positron.

    The effective cross section for the excitation of an electron pair for which one electron has the energy E (the other has energy $k - E$) by a light quanta of energy k is, for $k \gg mc^2$, according to Bethe and Heitler (B 16),

$$dQ = 4Z^2 \frac{e^2}{\hbar c}\left(\frac{e^2}{mc^2}\right)^2 \frac{dE}{k}\left[\left(\frac{E}{k}\right)^2 + \left(1 - \frac{E}{k}\right)^2 + \frac{2}{3}\frac{E}{k}\left(1 - \frac{E}{k}\right)\right]\log\frac{183}{Z^{1/3}} \tag{7}$$

+ smaller terms.

    The bracketed factor equals 1 for $E = 0$ and $E = k$; it has the value 2/3 for $E = k/2$. Therefore, again, one can take it as a constant without too great an error, i.e., assume that the primary energy is divided between the two electrons in all ratios with equal probability. If the formula is integrated over E and multiplied by N, one obtains for the probability that one pair is produced by a light quantum on the path increment dx or dl respectively

$$dn = \frac{7}{9}\frac{dx}{x_0} = \frac{7}{9}dl = \delta dl. \tag{8}$$

where $7/9$ is abbreviated by δ.

c) **Ionization.** Through the interplay of radiation-by-collision and pair formation a cascade is generated by an energetic primary particle which continues to grow until the energies of the component particles become too small. The limiting energy is defined as that at which the energy lost by ionization begins to predominate over that lost by radiation. Thus, if an electron produced by pair formation has so little energy that on the next radiation unit path length x_0 which it traverses it loses most of its energy by ionization, then its further contribution to the cascade is to be neglected within the approximation of the present calculations. We consider, therefore, that the cascade development is broken off if the energy of the electron is equal to the energy lost by ionization per radiation unit of distance. This we will call E_J. In the simple approximation we assume that, for $E > E_J$, the ionization loss can be neglected, while for $E < E_J$, the radiation loss is negligible. More precise investigations by Arley have shown that, with this approximation, errors up to 50% can be introduced.

Thus we may write

$$E_J = x_0\left(\frac{dE}{dx}\right)_{\text{Ion.}} = \left(\frac{dE}{dl}\right)_{\text{Ion.}} \tag{9}$$

The ionization loss per cm. is proportional to the number of electrons per c.c., or to Z, whereas x_0 is inversely proportional to Z^2. Therefore E_J is nearly proportional to $1/Z$. An approximate interpolation formula is

$$E_J = \frac{1600mc^2}{Z}. \tag{10}$$

A table of E_J is given in the following chapter by Molière (page 33).

2. The Fundamental Equations of the Cascade Theory

We now consider the formation of a cascade. We simplify the calculation by the assumption that all particles are emitted exactly in the forward direction so that the number of particles will be considered as a function only of the path traversed and not of the angle of deflection as well. The angular scattering is dealt with in the next chapter by G. Molière. Our procedure closely parallels a treatment of Landau and Rumer (L 2). We introduce the following symbols:

$F(E,l)$ = number of electrons of an energy $>E$ at distance l from the starting point of the cascade,

$G(E,l)$ = number of light quanta of energy $>E$ at distance l.

The numbers of electrons and of light quanta between the energies E and $E + dE$ are then given, respectively, by

$$\left. \begin{aligned} f(E,l)dE &= -\frac{\partial F(E,l)}{\partial E}dE, \\[2mm] g(E,l)dE &= -\frac{\partial G(E,l)}{\partial E}dE. \end{aligned} \right\} \tag{11}$$

If these particles traverse the path segment dl, the number of electrons is changed according to the equation

$$F(E,l + dl) = F(E,l) - dF(E,l)_{\text{rad.}} + dF(E,l)_{\text{pair}}, \tag{12}$$

where $dF(E,l)_{\text{rad}}$ is the number of electrons whose energy drops below E along the segment dl because of radiation losses, and $dF(E,l)_{\text{pair}}$ is the number of electrons of energy greater than E which appear on this segment by pair formation. Since an electron of energy $E' > E$ loses an energy greater than $E' - E$ with the probability $dl \int_{E'-E}^{E'} dk/k$, then

$$dF(E,l)_{\text{rad}} = \int_{E}^{\infty} dE' f(E',l) \cdot dl \cdot \int_{E'-E}^{E'} \frac{dk}{k}. \tag{13}$$

On the other hand, a light quantum of energy E' excites, according to (8), $2\,\delta dl$ electrons whose energies lie with equal probability in the range $0 - E'$. Here we are interested, however, only in the fraction which lie in the range E to E'. Therefore:

$$dF(E,l)_{\text{pair}} = \int_{E}^{\infty} dE' g(E',l) \cdot 2\delta dl \frac{E' - E}{E'}. \tag{14}$$

Analogously we obtain for the change in the number of light quanta

$$G(E,l + dl) = G(E,l) - \delta \cdot dl\, G(E,l) + \int_{E}^{\infty} dE' f(E',l) \cdot dl \int_{E}^{E'} \frac{dk}{k}. \tag{15}$$

If we introduce $\partial F/\partial E$ and $\partial G/\partial E$ in (12) and (15) in place of f and y, divide through by dl, and transform the resulting expressions by partial integration, whereby it is assumed that $F = G = 0$ for $E' = \infty$, then we obtain the fundamental equations of the cascade theory.

$$\frac{\partial F(E,l)}{\partial l} = -\int_E^\infty [F(E',l) - F(E,l)]dE'\left(\frac{1}{E'} - \frac{1}{E' - E}\right)$$

$$+ 2\delta \int_E^\infty G(E',l) \, dE' \frac{E}{E'^2},$$ (16)

$$\frac{\partial G(E,l)}{\partial l} = -\delta \cdot G(E,l) + \int_E^\infty F(E',l)\frac{dE'}{E'}.$$

3. Solution for a Power Spectrum

The integro-differential equations have two properties which make it easy to find a special solution: (1) they are linear in F and G so that the sum of two solutions is also a solution, (2) they are homogeneous in E and E' so that one can write

$$\frac{E'}{E} = \xi$$ (17)

and obtain an equation depending only on ξ and l.

We write
$$F(E,l) = F(l) \cdot E^{-s},$$
$$s > 0$$ (18)
$$G(E,l) = G(l) \cdot E^{-s},$$

and obtain for $F(l)$ and $G(l)$ the differential equations

$$\left. \begin{aligned} \frac{dF(l)}{dl} &= F'(l) = -\sigma(s)F(l) + 2\delta \frac{G(l)}{s+1}, \\[2mm] \frac{dG(l)}{dl} &= G'(l) = -\delta G(l) + \frac{F(l)}{s}. \end{aligned} \right\}$$ (19)

These equations no longer depend upon ξ. Therefore, if a power spectrum obtains for $l = 0$ it will also have the same form for all values of l. $\sigma(s)$ is the following integral:

$$\sigma(s) = \int_1^\infty \left(\frac{1}{\xi^s} - 1\right)\left(\frac{1}{\xi} - \frac{1}{\xi - 1}\right)d\xi = C + \psi(s).$$ (20)

$C = 0.577$ is the Euler constant, ψ is the logarithmic derivative of the gamma function.

$$\psi(s) = \frac{\partial}{\partial s}\log\Gamma(s + 1).$$ (21)

ψ also has the property that

$$\psi(s + 1) = \psi(s) + \frac{1}{s}.$$ (22)

Also it is noted that

$$\sigma(1) = 1, \qquad \sigma(2) = \tfrac{3}{2}, \qquad \sigma(3) = \tfrac{11}{8}$$

and

$$\lim_{s \to \infty} \sigma(s) = \log s + 0.577. \tag{23}$$

In order to solve equation (19) we write

$$\left. \begin{aligned} F(l) &= a_1 e^{-\kappa_1 l} + a_2 e^{-\kappa_2 l}, \\ G(l) &= b_1 e^{-\kappa_1 l} + b_2 e^{-\kappa_2 l}. \end{aligned} \right\} \tag{24}$$

When substituted in (19) this gives the conditional equations

$$\left. \begin{aligned} [\kappa - \sigma(s)]a + \frac{2\delta}{s+1}b &= 0, \\ \frac{a}{s} + (\kappa - \delta)\, b &= 0, \end{aligned} \right\} \tag{25}$$

which give the relations between a_1, b_1 and κ_1 or a_2, b_2, κ_2, respectively.

It follows that

$$\frac{a}{b} = s(\delta - \kappa), \tag{26}$$

with the double solution

$$\kappa_{1;2} = \frac{\sigma + \delta}{2} \pm \left[\left(\frac{\sigma - \delta}{2} \right)^2 + \frac{2\delta}{s(s+1)} \right]^{\tfrac{1}{2}}. \tag{27}$$

The following table shows how the solutions run:

s	0	1	∞
κ_1	$+\infty$	$1 + \delta$	$\log s + 0.577$
κ_2	$-\infty$	0	δ

If one expresses a in terms of b and κ it is found that

$$\left. \begin{aligned} F(l) &= b_1 s(\delta - \kappa_1)e^{-\kappa_1 l} + b_2 s(\delta - \kappa_2)e^{-\kappa_2 l}, \\ G(l) &= b_1 e^{-\kappa_1 l} + b_2 e^{-\kappa_2 l}. \end{aligned} \right\} \tag{28}$$

Intuitively, our result has the following meaning: The number of particles in a cascade which initially has a power spectrum is given by the sum of two exponential functions. Of the two exponents, the larger, κ_1, is always positive; the contribution represented by it, therefore, decreases continuously with increasing l and always at a greater rate than the other contribution. It represents the regenerative processes which come into prominence if the relative numbers of electrons and photons are not initially the same as would exist in a self-constituted completed cascade. For example, one can represent a cascade which initially possesses only electrons and no photons if one writes $b_1 = -b_2$. To the rapid decrease of the terms with κ_1 there then corresponds an increase of $G(l)$ with l until the first term has become vanishingly small, and then the course of G is governed by the second term only. κ_2 is negative for $s < 1$, positive for $s > 1$, and zero for $s = 1$. The value of the exponent determines whether the number of particles in the cascade increases or decreases. This is the physical significance. The energy content of the cascade as a whole is

$$E_K = \int [f(E) + g(E)]E\,dE \sim \int E^{-s}\,dE. \qquad (29)$$

This integral diverges logarithmically for $s = 1$, it diverges at the upper limit for $s < 1$, and it diverges at the lower limit for $s > 1$. The divergence at the lower limit is physically without significance since actually the cascade spectrum stops at E_J. A cascade with $s > 1$ has, therefore, a finite energy content, which must gradually become exhausted on account of the constant loss with increasing l of those particles whose energy is less than E_J. On the other hand a cascade with $s < 1$ would have an infinitely large reserve of energy in the high range from which a given energy interval would continuously gain more than it would lose to the lower range. In nature we naturally have only cascades with finite total energies, i.e., spectra with $s < 1$ cannot extend to arbitrarily large energies. After an initial increase in the number of particles there must be a succeeding decrease. The primary spectrum of the cosmic rays can apparently be represented in good approximation by a power law with $s = 1.8$. The cosmic rays in the atmosphere must, therefore, be a cascade with the number of particles decreasing exponentially with depth. According to (27), for $s = 1.8$, $\kappa_1 = 1.74$ and $\kappa_2 = 0.46$. The final decrease must, therefore, be represented by $e^{-0.46l}$, i.e., a decrease to the eth part every 2 radiation units ($3/4\ m\ H_2O$). For the soft component below the maximum this condition is rather well satisfied, a fact which thus confirms the cascade character of this component. The fact that a maximum of the intensity occurs in the high atmosphere must be attributed to a deviation of the primary spectrum from the power characteristic. A satisfactory explanation is already offered by the fact that charged particles of less than a certain energy cannot penetrate the earth's magnetic field. According to recent investigations, moreover, the primary rays appear to consist not principally of electrons but of protons; hence, the cascade theory, in the form developed here, is to be applied only to that part of the radiation which definitely consists of electrons and light quanta, i.e., to the soft component from the maximum on downwards.

4. The Formation of a Single Cascade

We now abandon the assumption that the spectrum originally has the power characteristic and calculate the building up of a cascade which is initiated by a single electron of a given energy. In this we follow the attack of Landau and Rumer (L 2).

We introduce two new functions of the parameter s through the equations

$$
\left.
\begin{aligned}
f(s,l) &= \int_0^\infty dE\; E^s f(E,l), \\
g(s,l) &= \int_0^\infty dE\; E^s g(E,l).
\end{aligned}
\right\}
\tag{30}
$$

These functions have the same significance in the resolution of the functions $f(E,l)$ and $g(E,l)$ into a power spectrum E^{-s} as Fourier coefficients have in the resolution into trigonometric functions. The new functions $f(s,l)$ and $g(s,l)$ satisfy the same differential equations as our earlier functions $F(l)$ and $G(l)$, i.e., the equation (19). According to (28), we can, therefore, write down the solutions immediately:

$$
\left.
\begin{aligned}
f(s,l) &= b_1 s \cdot (\delta - \kappa_1)e^{-\kappa_1 l} + b_2 s \cdot (\delta - \kappa_2)e^{-\kappa_2 l}, \\
g(s,l) &= b_1 e^{-\kappa_1 l} + b_2 e^{-\kappa_2 l}.
\end{aligned}
\right\}
\tag{31}
$$

Here it is to be observed that b_1 and b_2 are functions of the parameter s. If, initially, $(l = 0)$, no light quanta are present, then

$$
b_2 = -b_1 = b(s).
\tag{32}
$$

If at the start there is just one electron present with energy E_0, then the incident spectrum can be described by

$$
f(E, l = 0) = \delta(E - E_0).
\tag{33}
$$

The function $\delta(x)$ here signifies the Dirac singularity function which is defined by the two equations

$$
\left.
\begin{aligned}
\delta(x) &= 0 \text{ for } x \neq 0, \\
\int_{-\epsilon}^{+\epsilon} \delta(x)dx &= 1 \text{ for any } \epsilon.
\end{aligned}
\right\}
\tag{34}
$$

Therefore,

$$
f(s,0) = E_0^s.
\tag{35}
$$

From (31) it follows that

$$b(s) = \frac{E_0}{s(\kappa_1 - \kappa_2)}. \tag{36}$$

This put back again into (31) gives

$$\left.\begin{aligned}
f(s,l) &= \frac{E_0^s}{\kappa_1 - \kappa_2}[-(\delta - \kappa_1)e^{-\kappa_1 l} + (\delta - \kappa_2)e^{-\kappa_2 l}], \\
\\
g(s,l) &= \frac{E_0^s}{s(\kappa_1 - \kappa_2)}[-e^{-\kappa_1 l} + e^{-\kappa_2 l}].
\end{aligned}\right\} \tag{37}$$

In the bracketed factors we can neglect the term in $e^{-\kappa_1 l}$. Since, initially, only one particle is present, and κ_1 is always positive, this term is always less than 1; on the other hand, we are interested in actual showers where the number of particles is large compared to 1.

We introduce the following abbreviations.

$$\left.\begin{aligned}
\log\frac{E_0}{E} &= y, \\
\\
E \cdot f(E,l) &= e^{\varphi(y,l)}
\end{aligned}\right\} \tag{38}$$

and obtain from (37) by neglecting $e^{-\kappa_1 l}$, and from (30)

$$\int_0^\infty dy\, e^{\varphi(y,l)-ys} = \frac{\delta - \kappa_2}{\kappa_1 - \kappa_2}e^{-\kappa_2 l}. \tag{39}$$

We will now carry through an approximate calculation to determine φ and f respectively from this integral equation. The integrand has a sharp maximum at a value of y which we designate as y_m. As we will see later, this maximum is the steeper, the larger the number of particles that are formed. y_m is determined from the condition

$$\left(\frac{\partial\varphi}{\partial y}\right)_m - s = 0. \tag{40}$$

We develop $\varphi(y)$ in the neighborhood of the maximum (saddle point method):

$$\varphi(y) - ys = \varphi(y_m) - sy_m + \tfrac{1}{2}\varphi''(y_m)(y - y_m)^2, \tag{41}$$

taking into account only the terms included above and integrating from $-\infty$ instead of from 0. Thus we obtain for the integral the approximate expression.

$$e^{\varphi(y_m)-sy_m}\left(\frac{2\pi}{-\varphi''(y_m)}\right)^{\frac{1}{2}} = \frac{\delta - \kappa_2}{\kappa_1 - \kappa_2}e^{-\kappa_2 l} \tag{42}$$

or by taking the logarithm

$$\varphi(y_m) - sy_m + \kappa_2 l = \chi(s, y_m), \qquad (43)$$

in which

$$\chi(s, y_m) = \log\left[\frac{\delta - \kappa_2}{\kappa_1 - \kappa_2} \cdot \left(\frac{-\varphi''(y_m)}{2\pi} \right)^{\frac{1}{2}} \right]. \qquad (44)$$

We now drop the index m. Differentiating (43) with respect to s we obtain, together with (43) itself and with (40), the three equations

I. $\qquad \varphi(y, l) - sy + \kappa_2(s)l = \chi(s, y),$

II. $\qquad -y + \kappa_2'(s)l = \dfrac{\partial \chi(s, y)}{\partial s},$ $\qquad (45)$

III. $\qquad \dfrac{\partial \varphi(y, l)}{\partial y} - s = 0.$

Before we solve these equations let us picture to ourselves their meaning. The original equation (30) holds for all values of s. The equations (45) now relate each value of s to a given value of y. The equation (45, III) means, for instance, that y is that position in the spectrum where $F(E, l)$ behaves as a function of E, of the form E^{-s}. From equations (II) and (III) we can compute s as a function of y and l. We know in this way with what power of E the function F may be approximated at each position l and in the vicinity of each energy value E. If we put this value of s in (I), we then obtain an expression for $\varphi(y, l)$ itself and can thereby also calculate f and F directly. Since in the end we wish to know only F, we will not calculate s, φ, and f explicitly but construct the right combination of these values immediately.

$\chi(s, y)$ as a logarithm is slowly variable with s. We, therefore, neglect the right side of (II). When we differentiate (II) with respect to s we obtain

$$\frac{\partial y}{\partial s} = \kappa_2'' l + \text{small terms}. \qquad (46)$$

By differentiation of (III) with respect to y and by taking (46) into account, it follows that

$$\frac{\partial^2 \varphi}{\partial y^2} = \frac{\partial s}{\partial y} = \frac{1}{\kappa_2'' l}. \qquad (47)$$

This we introduce into (44) and obtain

$$\chi(s, y) = \log\left[\frac{\delta - \kappa_2}{\kappa_1 - \kappa_2} \cdot \left(\frac{1}{2\pi l \mid \kappa_2'' \mid} \right)^{\frac{1}{2}} \right] \qquad (48)$$

and

$$\frac{\partial \chi(s,y)}{\partial s} = \frac{\partial}{\partial s} \log \frac{\delta - \kappa_1}{\kappa_1 - \kappa_2} + \frac{1}{2} \frac{\kappa_2'''}{\kappa_2''}, \qquad (49)$$

which, when introduced into (45 II), results in an equation for s.

In the following we interest ourselves in the total number $n_{el}(l)$ of electrons in a cascade after traversal of a layer of matter of thickness l,

$$n_{el}(l) = F(E_J) = \int_{E_J}^{\infty} f(E,l)dE = \int_0^{y_J} e^{\varphi(y,l)}dy, \qquad (50)$$

where

$$y_J = \log \frac{E_0}{E_J}. \qquad (51)$$

For $E \geq 10^{10} eV$, $y_J \geq 5$. $\varphi(y,l)$ increases rapidly with y; we can, therefore, write with good approximation

$$n_{el}(l) = \int_0^{y_J} dy \cdot \exp \left[\varphi(y_J,l) + \left(\frac{\partial \varphi}{\partial y} \right)_{y_J} (y - y_J) \right]$$

$$= \left[e^{\varphi(y_J,l)} \Big/ \left(\frac{\partial \varphi}{\partial y} \right)_{y_J} \right] \left(1 - e^{-\left(\frac{\partial \varphi}{\partial y}\right)_{y_J} \cdot y_J} \right). \qquad (52)$$

According to (45, III) $(\partial \varphi / \partial y)_{y_J} = s(y_J,l)$. Since s is of the order of magnitude of 1 and y is appreciably greater than 1, we can neglect in satisfactory approximation the second term in the factor and obtain

$$n_{el}(l) = e^{\varphi(y_J,l)}/s(y_J,l). \qquad (53)$$

5. Evaluation of Results

a) **The Position of the Cascade Maximum.**   The number of electrons of a cascade must at first increase and then decrease. We designate by l_{max} the value at which the number reaches a maximum. $s(y_J,l)$ is a slowly varying function of l. Therefore, the maximum of $n_{el}(l)$ coincides approximately with that of $e^{\varphi(y_J,l)}$. Finally, there is not much importance to be attached to the precise value of l_{max}, since the function n_{el} passes through a very flat maximum. We, therefore, postulate

$$\left(\frac{\partial \varphi(y_J,l)}{\partial l} \right)_{l_{max}} = 0. \qquad (54)$$

From (45, I) one gets, by neglecting the right side,

$$\frac{\partial \varphi(y_J,l)}{\partial l} = y \frac{\partial s}{\partial l} - \kappa_2 - \frac{\partial \kappa_2}{\partial s} l \frac{\partial s}{\partial l}. \qquad (55)$$

The sum of the first and last terms of the right side of (55) is, according to (45, II), about equal to zero. Therefore, there remains

$$\kappa_2\,(l_{max}) \approx 0. \tag{56}$$

According to (27), this means that

$$s(y_J, l_{max}) \approx 1. \tag{57}$$

This is to be intuitively interpreted as meaning that as long as $s < 1$ for $E = E_J$ the number of particles continues to increase, but when $s > 1$, the number decreases in accordance with the results of the pure power spectrum. The region near E_J, however, contributes most abundantly to the number of particles of the whole cascade. For $s = 1$

$$\kappa_1 = 1.78, \quad \kappa_2 = 0, \quad \kappa_2' = 0.98, \quad \kappa_2'' = -1.41, \quad \kappa_2''' = 2.83, \tag{58}$$

$$\frac{\partial \chi}{\partial s} = +0.6.$$

If we put the above values in (45 II), and, in line with the adopted approximation, neglect the right side, it follows that

$$l_{max} = \frac{1}{\kappa_2'}\,y_J = 1.02\,\log \frac{E_0}{E_J}. \tag{59}$$

b) **The Number of Electrons and Light Quanta at the Maximum.**
From (48 I) it follows that

$$\varphi(y_J, l_{max}) = [sy_J - \kappa_2 l_{max} + \chi(s)]_{s=1} = y_J + \log 0.13 - \log (l_{max})^{\frac{1}{2}}. \tag{60}$$

whence

$$n_{el}(l_{max}) = \frac{0.13}{(l_{max})^{\frac{1}{2}}} \cdot \frac{E_0}{E_J}. \tag{61}$$

While l_{max}, therefore, changes only logarithmically with the initial energy, the size of the cascade at the maximum is proportional to the ratio of the initial to the ionization energy. Both conclusions were to be expected intuitively. The distance of the maximum from the starting point is proportional to the number of collisions required for the initial energy quantum E_0 to divide itself into quanta of the order of magnitude E_J. Since each collision about halves the energy the number of collisions is proportional to $\log (E_0/E_J)$. On the other hand, the size of the cascade at the maximum is given by the number of quanta of size E_J into which E_0 can be split.

According to (37), the ratio of the number of light quanta to the number of electrons is

$$\frac{n_q}{n_{el}} \approx \frac{1}{s(\delta - \kappa_2)}. \tag{62}$$

But at the maximum $s = 1$ and $\kappa_2 = 0$ so, because $\delta = 7/9$,

$$n_q(\mathrm{max}) \approx \tfrac{9}{7} n_{el}(\mathrm{max}). \tag{63}$$

c) **Approximation Formulae for the Development of a Cascade.** According to (53) and (45 I), if we abbreviate y_J with y,

$$n_{el}(l) = \frac{e^{\varphi(y,l)}}{s} \tag{64}$$

with

$$\varphi(y,l) = sy - \kappa_2(s)l + \chi(s). \tag{65}$$

According to (45 II)

$$y = \kappa_2'(s)l - \chi'(s). \tag{66}$$

For κ_2 and $\chi(s)$ we now make the approximations, which are sufficiently precise in the interesting range $1 \leq s \leq 3$:

$$\kappa_2 = 1 - \frac{1}{s}, \qquad \chi = -\frac{\alpha}{s} - \beta s - \frac{1}{2}\log l \tag{67}$$

with

$$\alpha = 1.4, \qquad \beta = 0.56.$$

From this it follows that

$$s = \left(\frac{l - \alpha}{y - \beta}\right)^{\frac{1}{2}}, \tag{68}$$

and

$$n_{el}(l) = \left(\frac{y - \beta}{l - \alpha}\right)^{\frac{1}{2}} \cdot \frac{1}{(l)^{\frac{1}{2}}} \cdot e^{-l + 2[(l-\alpha)(y-\beta)]^{1/2}}. \tag{69}$$

The essential part of the expression is the exponential factor. The whole expression is valid only for large values of l. In this case the root in the exponent predominates with increasing l, and the more so the larger y is; the number of electrons then increases exponentially. Finally, however, the term $-l$ dominates the expression, and the cascade is absorbed as e^{-l}. For the light quanta, according to (62) and (67), it follows that

$$n_q = \frac{n_{el}}{1 - \frac{2}{9}s}. \tag{70}$$

At the start of the cascade there are about as many light quanta as electrons; from the maximum on, the light quanta become more and more predominant.

d) The Number of Electrons with $E < E_J$. According to Arley (A 5), one can make the following evaluation: We assume that after an electron has reached the energy E_J it radiates no more but loses energy only through ionization. Since E_J was defined as the point where, according to a more exact calculation, the loss of energy by radiation was equal to that by ionization, the electron must continue its course for another radiation unit before it has lost all of its energy by ionization. Since the energy drop by ionization is proportional to the distances covered, the electrons which have energy $E < E_J$ have, therefore, traversed a fraction $\epsilon = 1 - E/E_J$ of a radiation unit since they had the energy E_J. Thus it follows that

$$f(E,l)\ dE_{(E<E_J)} = dE \cdot \begin{cases} f\left(E_J, l - \left[1 - \dfrac{E}{E_J}\right]\right) & \text{for } l \geq 1 - \dfrac{E}{E_J} \\[3mm] 0 & \text{for } l < 1 - \dfrac{E}{E_J}. \end{cases} \tag{71}$$

If we develop f in the vicinity of l one finds

$$f(E,l) = f(E_J,l)\left\{1 - \epsilon\frac{\partial}{\partial l} \log f(E_J,l)\right\}. \tag{72}$$

We construct the number n_{el}^* of all electrons under E_J:

$$n_{el}^* = \int_0^{E_J} f(E,l)dE = E_J f(E_J,l)\left\{1 - \frac{1}{2}\frac{\partial}{\partial l}\log f(E_J,l)\right\}$$
$$= e^{\varphi(y,\,l)}\left(1 + \frac{\kappa_2}{2}\right). \tag{73}$$

With the approximation used above, this leads to the formula analogous to (53)

$$n_{el}^* = \left(\frac{3}{2} - \frac{1}{2s}\right)e^{\varphi(y,\,l)} = \left(\frac{3s}{2} - \frac{1}{2}\right)n_{el}. \tag{74}$$

In particular, therefore, at the cascade maximum ($s \approx 1$) the number of electrons of energy under E_J is about as large as the number of electrons above E_J.

3. THE LARGE AIR SHOWERS

By G. Molière, Berlin-Dahlem

In the foregoing chapter the cascade theory was presented in so far as
it had to do with the actual development of the cascade, i.e., with the
multiplication of particles and the partition of energy. For this purpose
the angular scattering could be completely neglected and the calculations
carried out as though all cascade particles preserved without deviation the
direction of the original particle which unleashed the cascade. The recogni-
tion of this angular scattering and the computation of the angular and
spatial distribution of cascade particles induced by it require an extension
of the theory which is to concern us in the following treatment. The most
essential application of this is in regard to experiments which have to do
with the extensive showers as the most important cascade phenomenon.
(See the final section of this Chapter, p. 37).

1. Qualitative Picture of the Shower

Before we engage in the calculations themselves, let us attempt a qualitative picture of the cascade showers: The complete neglect of the angular
deflection represents the characteristic starting point of most theories,
and the shower is regarded as maintaining the precise direction of the
initiating primary particle. However, it cannot be said that only small
deflections occur; for example, in cascade showers in lead, large angular
divergences may occur throughout. For the progressive development of a
cascade from place to place the greatest importance attaches to the relatively small number of particles of high energy, which have practically no
angular deflection and are spatially concentrated in the dense core of the
shower. On the other hand, the particles of low energy, which are present
in superior numbers and contribute in largest measure to the spatial and
angular expansion of the shower, play only a small part in the further
development of the cascade. As the shower progresses from place to place,
these lose their energy rapidly and completely while, simultaneously,
through cascade processes new particles of low energy are supplied from
the core of the shower. This goes on until the energy reserve in the core is
spent. From what has been said, it follows that the spatial and angular
widths of the shower vary only slightly along the path of the shower. The
number of particles passing through a surface of unit area is very great at
the core and even approaches infinity at the center; towards the outside

it falls steadily off, and corresponding statements also hold for the angular distribution.

2. Previous Calculations

Euler and Wergeland (E 8) were the first to attack the problem of the angular and spatial distribution of particles in a cascade shower. This work gave the main features of the relationships in showers; in details their results can, on the whole, be improved quantitatively and, in part, also qualitatively because of their neglect of various effects the influence of which has been estimated by the author. These are:

a) the neglect of the large statistical fluctuations of energy loss suffered along their paths by the shower electrons through the emission of quanta by collision,

b) the neglect of the contribution of earlier generations to the deflection of shower particles of later generations,

c) the assumption of a Gaussian function for the spatial and angular distribution of the particles of equal energy in a shower.

For calculating the mean square of the spatial and angular deviations in a shower, a method in which these factors are not neglected has been given by L. Landau (L 1); however, the numerical results of this author are incorrect because of computational errors in the numerical data. The form of the distribution function was not investigated by Landau. We have, therefore, repeated the calculation of Euler and Wergeland by a more accurate procedure, which is to be attributed in part to Landau. (Molière (M 4)). The most important results of these calculations were a greater spatial extension of the shower by a factor of 3.4 and, at the same time, a stronger branching of the core of the shower than was given by the work of Euler and Wergeland. Similar results are also contained in a note by H. A. Bethe (B 15).

3. The Source of Angular Scattering

Practically the only source of angular deflection of the shower particles which has been taken into account by all authors is the Rutherford scattering of the shower electrons in the electrostatic fields of the atoms. The mean square of the change in angle which an electron of a given energy E suffers in a given path distance, in consequency of Rutherford scattering, has been calculated by Williams (W 9) and can be written, with reference to Euler and Wergeland, in the form

$$d(\overline{\theta^2}) = \frac{K^2}{E^2} dl \qquad (K \cong 2 \cdot 10^7 \text{ eV}). \tag{1}$$

Here dl is a small element of the path of the electron measured in radiation units x_0. —In addition to the Rutherford scattering, other sources of angular scattering also exist, including the process of pair formation and quantum emission by collision as well as the Compton processes of the light quanta along their paths. The angular deflections which are introduced by these processes per radiation unit, according to the estimates of Euler and Wergeland, are smaller by a power of ten than those given by (1). Since we have to deal with the sums of the squares of the angles, the other sources of scattering amount to about 1% of (1).

4. The Mean Square Deviations

The angular deflection and the spatial separation of the particles from the shower axis are described by the two dimensional vectors $\vec{\theta}$ and $\mathfrak{r}$ in the plane perpendicular to the axis. (Here it is assumed that the angles occurring in practice are so small that it is not necessary to distinguish between the angle and its sine). Because of the cylindrical symmetry of the problem, the angular and spatial distribution of the particles in the shower are characterized in the main by the mean square of their deflections $\vec{\theta}$ and $\mathfrak{r}$. To this we may also add the mixed mean square of the deflections $\overline{(\vec{\theta},\mathfrak{r})}$, which characterizes the coupling between the spatial and angular deflections. The process of reaching a state given by the mean square deflections of the particles of a given energy at a point in a shower is briefly explained in what follows.

Just as with a projectile fired from a distance at a screen, so here a small change in angle $\delta\vec{\theta}$, experienced by an electron at a distance l from the point in the showers under consideration shows up as a spatial deviation $\delta\mathfrak{r} = l \cdot \delta\vec{\theta}$. The contribution from an element of path dl at distance l from the point under consideration to the mean square deviation of an electron of energy E is, therefore, according to (1):

$$d(\overline{\theta^2}) = K^2\overline{E'^{-2}}(l)dl, \tag{2a}$$

$$d(\overline{\vec{\theta},\mathfrak{r}}) = K^2\overline{E'^{-2}}(l)ldl \quad \text{and} \tag{2b}$$

$$d(\overline{r^2}) = K^2\overline{E'^{-2}}(l)l^2dl. \tag{2c}$$

Here $E'(l)(> E)$ is that energy which the electron had at the distance l back of the point under consideration, in view of the fact that it loses energy by the emission of radiation by collision on its path to the latter position. The expressions (2) are, therefore, to be averaged over all possible values of the energy $E'(l)$, taking account of the probability for energy loss by radiation by collision. (In Euler and Wergeland's calculation this procedure was simplified in that the mean value $\overline{E'^{-2}}(l)$ was replaced by $\overline{E'}^{-2}(l)$, which was the first of the neglected effects listed. At the point of the maximum development of the shower $\overline{E'^{-2}}(l) = e^{-5/6 l} E^{-2}$ and $\overline{E'^{-2}}(l) = e^{-2l} E^{-2}$. In adding up the contributions made by the separate path elements dl to the mean square deviation, one must take account of the fact that the electron has at one time been created in pair formation by a light quantum. The expressions (2) must, therefore, be multiplied by the age probability $Q(l)$ $(= e^{-l}$ at the maximum point of the shower). When one integrates the resulting expression between the limits $l = 0$ and $l = \infty$, he obtains the contribution of the last generation to the mean square deviation of an electron of energy E.—Finally, it is to be observed that every particle at its point of formation already has a spatial and angular deviation given it by its ancestor particles and representing the inheritance of its entire previous history. We will not go into this in greater detail here but list in the following Table I the results for the mean square deviation of shower particles of energy E.

Here θ is to be understood as measured in arc and r in radiation units; K is the constant for angular scattering given by (1). The difference between the second and the first columns of Table I rests entirely upon the improved energy statistics.

Table 1.

	According to EULER and WERGELAND	Exact Calculation		
		Electrons		Light quanta
		Portion from last generation	Total	Total
$\dfrac{E^2}{K^2}\overline{\theta^2}\,(E)$	0.333	0.545	0.6	0.2
$\dfrac{E^2}{K^2}\overline{(\vec{\theta},\,\mathbf{r})}\,(E)$	—	0.298	0.437	0.403
$\dfrac{E^2}{K^2}\overline{r^2}\,(E)$	0.074	0.162	0.835	1.314

Comparison of the second and third columns shows that, especially with $\overline{r^2}$, the contribution from past experience is very essential. After Landau's computational errors have been corrected, his method, mentioned in the beginning, gives the same or similar numerical values as those entered in columns 3 and 4 of the table, depending upon which form of the Bethe-Heitler equations are used. (cf. Chapter 2 by Heisenberg pages 12 to 13, eq. (1 and 7). Landau himself uses these equations in a somewhat more complicated form).

5. The Distribution Functions f(E,θ) and f(E,r)

In order to calculate the distribution functions for the angular and spatial dispersion of cascade particles, we start out with the integro-differential equations set up in the work of Landau cited above.

$$\frac{\partial f}{\partial l} = -Af + Bg + \frac{K^2}{4E^2}\Delta_\theta f - (\vec{\theta},\nabla_{\mathfrak{r}})f,$$

$$\frac{\partial g}{\partial l} = Cf - \frac{7}{9}g - (\vec{\theta},\nabla_{\mathfrak{r}})g. \qquad\qquad (3)$$

Here f and g are functions of E, $\vec{\theta}$ and $\mathfrak{r}$. In particular, the quantities in (3) have the following significance:

$f(E, \vec{\theta}, \mathfrak{r})dEd\tau_\theta d\tau_{\mathfrak{r}}$ is the number of electrons which strike surface element $d\tau_{\mathfrak{r}}$ at $\mathfrak{r}$ with an energy in the range dE at E and from a direction within the range $d\tau_\theta$ at $\vec{\theta}$;

$g(E, \vec{\theta}, \mathfrak{r})dEd\tau_\theta d\tau_{\mathfrak{r}}$ is the corresponding quantity for light quanta;

l is the path length in radiation units traversed by the shower;

A, B and C are integral operators which operate on E;

Δ_θ is the Laplace Operator in the $\vec{\theta}$ plane;

$\nabla_{\mathfrak{r}}$ is the gradient in the $\mathfrak{r}$ plane and

K is the constant in equation (1).

The equations (3) are the integro-differential equations of the cascade theory (similar to equation (16) p. 16 in Chapter 2, Heisenberg, but for the differential spectrum) completed by terms which describe the changes of f and g in consequence of the angular and positional changes of the particles.

The additional term for the angular variation, $\left(\frac{\partial f}{\partial l}\right)_\theta = \frac{K^2}{4E^2}\Delta f$ evidently has the form of a diffusion equation; the term with the operator $(\vec{\theta}, \nabla_{\mathfrak{r}})$ takes into consideration the change in position of the particles in consequence of the already existing angular deflections. For comparison with experiment it is sufficient to calculate the distribution function $f(E, \vec{\theta})$ (independent of $\mathfrak{r}$) and $f(E, \mathfrak{r})$ (independent of $\vec{\theta}$) for the point of maximum shower development. To this end we have taken the following course:

In the first place by the introduction of the new variables

$$\vec{\theta}' = \frac{2E}{K}\vec{\theta} \quad \text{and} \quad \mathfrak{r}' = \frac{2E}{K}\mathfrak{r}$$

one can make the integro-differential equations no longer dependent upon E

explicitly. At the same time these substitutions fulfill the condition that in the limiting case $K \to 0$ (i.e. with vanishing angular scattering) the distribution functions f and g take the form of δ-functions with respect to the variables $\vec{\Theta}$ and $\mathfrak{r}$. This means that the angular and spatial deviations of the ensemble of shower particles vanish, as must be the case since the shower has been developed by a single penetrating particle. Next the function $f(E, \vec{\Theta}', \mathfrak{r}')$ is converted by a fourfold Fourier-Transformation with respect to the variables $\vec{\Theta}'$ and $\mathfrak{r}'$ to a function $\varphi(E, \vec{\zeta}, \vec{\rho})$ [and, correspondingly, $g(E, \vec{\Theta}', \mathfrak{r}')$ is converted to $\psi(E, \vec{\zeta}, \vec{\rho})$] where $\vec{\zeta}$ is the new vector variable corresponding to $\vec{\Theta}'$ and $\vec{\rho}$ that corresponding to $\mathfrak{r}'$. From the form $E^{-2}dE$ for the energy spectrum at the maximum point, it follows that φ and ψ depend on E only through the factor $E^{-2} \cdot \left(\dfrac{2E}{K}\right)^4$ which we separate out in what follows. It suffices to know φ and ψ in those ranges of the argument in which $\vec{\zeta}$ and $\vec{\rho}$ have the same direction. On acount of the cylindrical symmetry of the problem one comes out with two independent scalar variables ζ and ρ. $\varphi(\zeta, 0)$ measures the angular distribution and $\varphi(0, \rho)$ the spatial distribution.

The relations for the angular distribution are the simplest. Here, if one puts $\rho = 0$ in the integro-differential equation and eliminates $\psi(\zeta)$, he obtains for $\varphi(\zeta)$ the purely integral equation

$$\int_0^\zeta \frac{\zeta\varphi(\zeta) - \zeta'\varphi(\zeta')}{\zeta - \zeta'}\, d\zeta' - \frac{2}{\zeta} \int_0^\zeta d\zeta' \int_0^{\zeta'} d\zeta''\varphi(\zeta'') + \zeta^3\varphi(\zeta) = 0, \quad (4)$$

which we use in the following manner for a step-wise determination of $\varphi(\zeta)$: In the first place one sees from the equation that $\varphi(\zeta)$ is always positive and falls off monotonically, and at large values of ζ as ζ^{-3}. Also one can derive from (4) the coefficients of the power series expansion of $\varphi(\zeta)$, from which the function is known in the initial range. Finally, the integral equation will be used in the following manner to form a numerical construction procedure for calculating the function $\varphi(\zeta)$: One divides the coordinate ζ into intervals of a convenient size ϵ; let ζ_n be the value of the function for the argument $\zeta = n\epsilon$ ($n = 0,1,2, \cdots$). One now expresses the integral in (4) approximately by summing over the index n. The summation equation obtained in this way from the integral equation can be regarded as a recursion formula for the function φ_n, from which the next term in sequence, φ_{n+1}, can be determined as soon as the series $\varphi_0, \varphi_1, \varphi_2 \cdots \varphi_n$ is known. The procedure can be carried through very precisely and forms the basis, in spite of the complicated form of the integral, for computing the function satisfactorily up to rather large values of the argument. The results of this calculation can be represented with a precision of about 1% by the interpolation formula

$$\varphi(\zeta) = \frac{a}{(1 + \alpha^2\zeta^2)^{3/2}} - \frac{a - 1}{(1 + \beta^2\zeta^2)^{5/2}} \tag{5}$$

with $a = 3.473$, $d = 1.05$ and $\beta = 0.912$.

From this one deduces by a Fourier-Transformation (which in this case involves the Bessel-Function J_0) the following expressions for the energy and angular distributions of the electrons:

$$f(E,\Theta) = \frac{2}{\pi K^2}\left[\frac{a}{\alpha^2} e^{\frac{-2E\Theta}{\alpha K}} - \frac{a - 1}{3\beta^2}\left(1 + \frac{2E\Theta}{\beta K}\right)e^{\frac{-2E\Theta}{\beta K}}\right] \tag{6}$$

with the same constants as (5).

The relations are more complex in the case of the spatial distribution. For this case also a construction procedure may be developed; however, one cannot make $\zeta = 0$ on apriori grounds, since the value of the function at $\zeta = 0$ depends upon the course of the function $\varphi(\zeta, \rho)$ when $\zeta \neq 0$. Therefore, one has to evaluate the course of the function in a suitable initial region of the ζ, ρ-plane with the help of various series expansions. Starting out with these one can then determine the further course of the function in the ζ, ρ-plane with the help of a construction procedure. The result of this calculation at $\zeta = 0$ can be represented with a precision of about 3% by the interpolation formula.

$$\varphi(\rho) = \frac{a}{(1 + \alpha^2\rho^2)^{5/6}} - \frac{a - 1}{(1 + \beta^2\rho^2)^{11/6}} \tag{7}$$

with $a = 2.8$, $\alpha^2 = 1.36$, and $\beta^2 = 0.71$. By a Fourier Transformation one obtains as the distribution function of electrons with respect to energy and spatial separation from the shower axis

$$f(E,r) = \frac{2}{\pi K^2}\left[\frac{a}{\alpha^2} Q_{-1/6}\left(\frac{2Er}{\alpha K}\right) - \frac{a - 1}{\beta^2} Q_{5/6}\left(\frac{2Er}{\beta K}\right)\right] \tag{8}$$

with the abbreviation

$$Q_p(x) = \frac{\frac{\pi}{2} \cdot \left(\frac{x}{2}\right)^p}{\Gamma(p + 1)} i^{p+1} H_p(ix),$$

where H_p signifies the Hankel Function of the first kind. The function $f(E, \Theta)$, according to (6), and $f(E, r)$, according to (8), are quite different from the Gauss function, especially the latter which varies as $r^{-1/3}$ near $r = 0$.—It should be further stated that all of these calculations, in particular the results (6) and (8), apply to the energy values $E > E_j$, where E_j is the limiting value, below which the cascade forming processes cease to be important and become submerged by the ionization.

6. The Distribution Functions $N(\Theta)$ and $N(r)$

Following Euler and Wergeland we designate by $N(\Theta)\Theta d\Theta$ and $N(r)r dr$ the relative numbers of electrons with an angular deflection between Θ and $\Theta + d\Theta$ and those with a spatial displacement from the shower axis between r and $r + dr$ respectively. The densities $N(\Theta)$ and $N(r)$ are approximately represented by Euler and Wergeland by means of the interpolation formulae

$$N(\Theta) = \frac{\text{const}}{\Theta} 2^{-\Theta/\Theta_h}, \qquad (9a)$$

and

$$N(r) = \frac{\text{const}}{r} 2^{-r/r_h}, \qquad (9b)$$

which we must now compare with our more accurate results. The half value angle Θ_h and distance r_h in (9) define the radius of the circle which encloses half of the shower electrons. For the following discussion it is expedient to use the angle and distance units introduced by Euler and Wergeland,

$$\Theta_1 = \frac{K}{E_j} \quad \text{and} \quad r_1 = \Theta_1 x_0 = \frac{K x_0}{E_j},$$

where x_0 signifies the radiation unit. For illustration the numerical values of E_j and x_0 for various substances, as well as the resulting values of Θ_1 and r_1 (in degrees and cm. respectively), are collected in the following table 2.

Table 2.

	Air	H_2O	Al	Fe	(Pb)	Units
$E_j =$	11.3	11.3	6.3	3.1	(1.0)	10^9 eV
$x_0 =$	33000	43	9.6	1.8	(0.51)	cm
$\Theta_1 =$	10.3°	10.3°	18.6°	37.7°	(116°)	angular degrees
$r_1 =$	5950	7 8	3.1	1.2	(1.0)	cm

As shown by the numbers in parentheses in the last column the assumption of small angles is no longer justified in the case of lead.

The portions contributed to the densities $N(\Theta)$ and $N(r)$ by electrons with energy $E > E_i$ are obtained from (6) and (8) respectively by integrating over E between the limits E_i and ∞. The portions from electrons with energies $E < E_i$ require a special treatment which we have based upon the Arley approximation (Arley (A 5)). The details of this somewhat complicated calculation are passed over. Finally, the contributions of single scattering to $N(\Theta)$ and $N(r)$ are taken into account. These result from the fact that occasionally a large angular deflection can take place in a single scattering act (cf. Williams (W 9)).

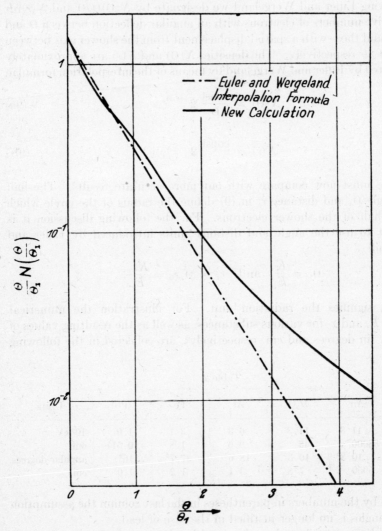

Fig. 1a. Angular distribution of shower electrons

The results of these calculations are presented in figures 1a and 1b, in which the functions $[\Theta/\Theta_1]N(\Theta/\Theta_1)$ and $[r/r_1]N(r/r_1)$ are plotted in logarithmic units in the solid curves. (The form of these curves should actually be somewhat smoother than represented in the figure; the slight waviness results from the approximations which were used in calculating the portion belonging to the energies $E < E_i$). The absolute ordinates of the curves and the numerical factor in the following asymptotic formulae are so chosen that the following normalization equations are valid:

$$\int_0^\infty N\left(\frac{\Theta}{\Theta_1}\right)\frac{\Theta}{\Theta_1}\,d\left(\frac{\Theta}{\Theta_1}\right) = 1 \quad \text{and} \quad \int_0^\infty N\left(\frac{r}{r_1}\right)\frac{r}{r_1}\,d\left(\frac{r}{r_1}\right) = 1.$$

a) **The Solid Angle Density** $N(\Theta/\Theta_1)$. The curve for $\Theta/\Theta_1\,N(\Theta/\Theta_1)$ in Fig. 1a is approximated in the region $0 \leq \Theta/\Theta_1 \lesssim 3$ with a precision of about 15% by a straight line (not shown), which represents the Euler-Wergeland interpolation formula (9a) with the half-value angle $\Theta_h = 0.55\Theta_1$. (The straight line plotted with dot-dash corresponds to the formula (9a) with the half angle of $0.47\Theta_1$ given by Euler and Wergeland). The asymptotic behavior of the solid-angle density for large arguments (Θ/Θ_1) is reproduced by

$$\frac{\Theta}{\Theta_1}N\left(\frac{\Theta}{\Theta_1}\right) \approx \left(\frac{\Theta}{\Theta_1}\right)^{-3}. \tag{10}$$

b) **The Spatial Density** $N(r/r_1)$. The curve representing the function $r/r_1\,N(r/r_1)$ in Fig. 1b is approximately reproduced for small arguments by the Euler-Wergeland linear interpolation corresponding to formula (9b) (dot-dash line; half-value distance $r_h = 0.24r_1$). For larger arguments the curve shows an appreciably slower rate of fall, corresponding to a half-value distance of about $r_h = 0.81r_1$.

Its asymptotic behavior for small r is described by[1]

$$\frac{r}{r_1}N\left(\frac{r}{r_1}\right) \approx 3.25\left[1 - 4.9\left(\frac{r}{r_1}\right)^{-2/3}\right]. \tag{11}$$

For large arguments (> 7) the contribution of single scattering to the spatial dispersion predominates. This contribution, which likewise de-

---

[1]In agreement with the results of EULER and WERGELAND, it follows from (11) that the density $N(r)$ has a singularity like r^{-1}. On the contrary, H. A. BETHE finds that the density varies at small r like $r^{-4/3}$. This form of the singularity results, as one can show, if the EULER-WERGELAND calculation is improved in only one respect, namely, that, instead of the electrons of equal energy, one assumes that just the electrons of equal energy and equal traversed path length are distributed according to a GAUSSIAN function. In agreement with us, BETHE also shows that the influence of earlier generations must be taken into account.

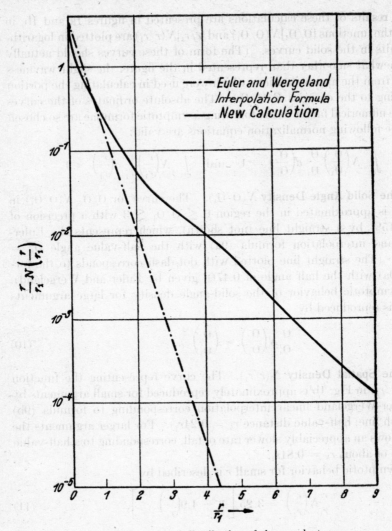

Fig. 1b. Spacial distribution of shower electrons

termines the asymptotic behavior of the whole function at large arguments, has the form

$$\frac{r}{r_1}N\left(\frac{r}{r_1}\right) \approx 0.1\left(\frac{r}{r_1}\right)^{-3}. \tag{12}$$

As one sees, the new calculation gives a larger sidewise dispersion of the shower, as well as a stronger compression of the shower core.

It is, likewise, to be expected that a better theory of the energy loss of electrons by ionization than is possible according to the above method will increase the shower breadth still further for the following reasons: The shower particles most strongly deflected to the side are those with relatively low energy, and the ratio of the number of particles of low energy to those of high energy can be evaluated, as has been pointed out by various authors (Belenky (B 7) and Schönberg (S 10)), by the usual approximations with which the stopping of electrons by ionization is calculated. Therefore, on the one hand, the usual neglecting of the energy losses due to ionization for electron energies $E > E_j$ leads to too large a number of particles in this region of high energy; on the other hand, (Belenky (B 7)), the Arley approximation gives too small a number of electrons in the low energy range in consequence of the neglect of those electrons which are excited by light quanta with an initial energy $E < E_j$.

7. Comparison with Experiment[1]

In the atmosphere very energetic penetrating particles set off extensive cascade showers, the so called "air showers," which among other ways can be detected by coincidence measurements of two or more spatially separated counter tubes. This type of coincidence was first observed in the year 1938 by Schmeiser and Bothe (S 9), with countertube separations up to a few tens of meters, and then by Auger (A 10), Kolhorster (K 4) and others with counter distances up to several hundred meters. Janossy and Lovell (J 4), as well as Auger, Maze, Ehrenfest and Freon (A 11), were able to establish through Wilson chamber photographs that these coincidences were set off by air showers. Although these Wilson photographs showed only electron tracks and no penetrating particles, it has been suggested from several quarters that the air showers might contain mesons as well as the cascade forming electrons and light quanta. Auger believed he had obtained a point of confirmation for this assumption in that he, as well as Kolhorster, found that about 25% of the coincidences still remained under 15 cm. of lead shielding. On the contrary, Janossy ventured the view that the great penetrating power of the coincidences could be explained on the assumption of pure cascade showers by the high energies of the particles. This view was supported by Euler and Wergeland through the further argument that the observed coincidences in the absorption measurements were for the most part set off by the dense shower cores, and that the probability of response of the counter tube to a bundle of many simultaneous rays was reduced in much smaller degree by the shielding than was the radiation density. To complete the argument it must be pointed out that the radiation density of a shower which just reaches its maximum after

---

[1]The following discussion closely follows EULER and WERGELAND.

penetrating the atmosphere is not really reduced to zero but only to about 0.5% by an additional 15 cm. of lead (which is equivalent to somewhat more than the thickness of the atmosphere) as is shown by a rough calculation based upon the approximation formulae given in the previous chapter by Heisenberg. (Eq. (69) and (74)).

Although Auger's grounds for the assumption of a mixture of mesons in the air showers do not seem compelling, Euler and Wergeland seem to have come to such an assumption in an effort to bring into agreement with experiment the frequencies of coincidence of pairs of counter tubes as a function of countertube separation, as computed by them on the basis of the cascade theory. In order to clarify this question a new calculation was carried through, the results of which are compared in Fig. 2 with the corresponding results of Euler and Wergeland on the one hand, and the results of measurements of Auger (A 9) on the other. As one sees, the new calculation gives good agreement with the experiments for countertube distances between 20 and 150 meters. The discrepancies outside of this range are to be attributed to the fact that postulates upon which the calculations are

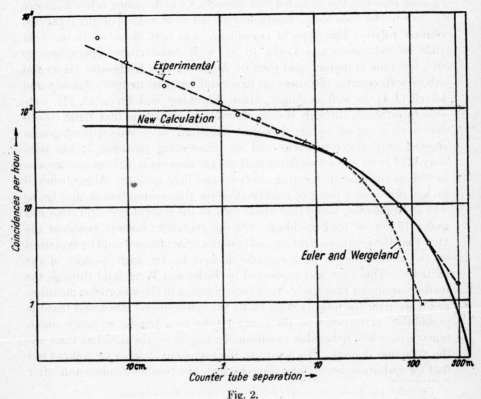

Fig. 2.

based are not valid there. In particular, the coincidences at small counter tube separations are excited predominantly by showers which have already passed their maximum, and for which the spatial electron distribution calculated for the maximum is no longer valid. The spatial distribution of particles in a shower can, therefore, be interpreted without the assumption of a hard radiation accompanying the shower. This also follows from experiments by Hilberry and by Auger[1], who were able to show that the radiation in the outer ranges of the large air showers is much softer than in the shower core. A primary spectrum of the form

$$H(E_0) = 0.04\left(\frac{10^{10}\text{eV}}{E_0}\right)^{1.8} \tag{13}$$

is taken as the basis for the calculations, (precisely as with Euler and Wergeland). The numerical factor 0.04 in this expression was determined by comparison with experiment. $H(E_0)$ in (13) signifies the number of primary electrons of energy greater than E_0 which strike one cm.^{2} per second from directions uniformly distributed over the unit hemisphere. (Here we formally take the position that the air showers are excited by primary electrons). Starting out with (13), and with the use of the approximation formula given by Heisenberg in the foregoing chapter for the size of the shower as a function of the primary energy and path length, the frequency distribution of shower size is determined. The approximate correctness of the exponent 1.8 in Eq. (13) is established up to energies $E_0 \approx 10^{15}$eV by the good agreement between calculation and experiment in the range of the data and by the approximate agreement of the numerical factor 0.04 with the determination from the total ionization. Mention may also be made of the experiments by Geiger and Stubbe (G 3) with 5- and 6-fold coincidences, in which an unexpectedly high coincidence rate was found at small counter tube separations, a fact which seems compatible with the strong compression of the shower core according to our new calculation.

In addition to the coincidence measurements with counter tubes and the experiments with the Wilson chamber, the ionization chamber also affords an important auxiliary means for studying the air showers. Here one finds the so-called Hoffman bursts, (i.e., the sudden appearance of a very large amount of ionization in the chamber) which are produced almost exclusively by air showers. The measurement of the frequency distribution of burst size constitutes an especially direct method for determining the energy spectrum of the shower-producing primary particles. Since, as already mentioned, the size of an air shower is approximately proportional to the

[1]Mentioned in the cited note by H. A. BETHE (B15).

energy of the primary particle which produces it, the energy spectrum itself
is reflected in the frequency distribution of the shower size.   Furthermore a
certain size of Hoffman burst is excited, *on the average*, by air showers of a
certain size.   The energy spectrum of the primary particles can, therefore,
be read directly from the frequency distribution of the burst sizes.   This
spectrum can be determined up to energy values of $3 \cdot 10^{10}$eV and it comes
out to be of the form $E_0^{-\gamma}$ with $\gamma = 1.85 \pm 0.2$ (according to Euler and
Wergeland).

H. Euler (E 5) has investigated these relationships more precisely on
the basis of the cascade theory of air showers and has compared his results
with the burst distribution curves according to the measurements of
Carmichael.   From certain details in the shape of these curves, he was able
to conclude that the small Hoffman bursts are caused predominantly, not
by air showers, but by nuclear disintegrations, which are induced in the
walls of the chamber by the hard radiation (cf. Chapter 13, Bagge).

MESONS

4. THE CREATION OF MESONS

By K. Wirtz, Berlin-Dahlem

1. Experimental Arguments for the Existence of Mesons

In the modern discussion of the penetrating component of the cosmic rays one starts out with the assumption that it consists in greatest part of mesons. The experimental arguments which have lead to this assumption are the following (Euler and Heisenberg (E 7)):

a) Various statistical studies have been made of measurements of the momenta of rays producing Wilson chamber tracks (Kunze (K 7), Blackett (B 22), Herzog and Scherrer (H 10) and Anderson (A 3)) with some of these momenta extending to $2 \cdot 10^{10}$eV. One finds here a spectrum of ionizing particles, which falls off continuously towards the high momenta. The tracks of most of the cosmic rays show an ionization which differs but little from that of an electron. Even in the case of particles with momenta $pc \leq 0.5 \cdot 10^9$eV, the tracks are so thin that their mass is certainly less than that of the proton. A small fraction, of the order of 0.1% (Anderson (A 3), Neddermeyer and Anderson (N 2)), shows thick tracks; these are protons. In making these arguments it is assumed that the charge of all particles is equal to the elementary electronic charge.

b) At low momenta, $<0.2 \cdot 10^9$eV the observed loss of momentum in lead is as great as for radiative electrons. It decreases, however, with increasing momentum, and at $0.5 \cdot 10^9$eV it amounts to only a tenth of the initial value. From this it follows that most of the particles above $0.2 \cdot 10^9$eV are heavier than electrons.

From the experimental fact that the particles between $0.2 \cdot 10^9 \leq pc \leq 0.5 \cdot 10^9$eV ionize less than protons and radiate less than electrons, Anderson and Neddermeyer (N 2) have concluded that particles of intermediate mass are present with the charge of an electron. This interpretation is now universally accepted in preference to the one put forth first that the radiation theory breaks down at energies $> 10^8$eV.

From measurements of curvature and the density of ionization along the track, the mass of the intermediate particle can be determined. Estimates to date place it in the range 160 to 240 electron masses (cf. Chapt. 8, Heisenberg). Thus far, there is no certain criterion that protons are not also present in large numbers in the very energetic tracks $> 0.5 \cdot 10^9$eV.

Moreover, it is not certain that there are not particles of various intermediate masses.

2. Yukawa Theory of the Meson and the Decrease of Meson Intensity at Great Heights

As is well known, these penetrating particles of medium weight have been associated with the particles postulated by Yukawa (Y 2 to Y 5) to explain the nuclear forces (cf. Chapter 10, v. Weizsacker), and attempts have been made to discuss them on the basis of this theory. An important consequence of the theory is that the mesons have a finite period of life, the experimental value of which is about 1.2 to $2.5 \cdot 10^{-6}$ second (cf. Chapter 8, Heisenberg); the meson then spontaneously decays into an electron and a neutrino. This spontaneous decay has also recently been observed in the Wilson chamber by Williams and Evans (W 11) and by Williams and Roberts (W 12). From this finite lifetime it follows that the mesons cannot come from external space but must be excited in the atmosphere by primary rays. This conclusion should be capable of direct experimental proof, for if it is right the meson intensity which is known to increase at first with height like the shower particles, should eventually diminish again at the top of the atmosphere.

This question has been attacked in several recent investigations. Fig. 1 is taken from a paper by Ehmert (E 2). It shows the hard (H) and the hard plus the soft components of the cosmic rays (Pfotzer (P 2 and P 3)) as functions of the amount of matter traversed, the former measured in a 3-fold coincidence arrangement which is sketched in the figure. This device was sent up in a balloon and was self-registering. The greatest height corresponded to 16 mm. Hg. One sees that the intensity of mesons between 100 and 16 mm. Hg. is nearly constant and is some 12 times as great as at sea level. The length of the dashes gives the pressure range flown through in 4 minutes, while the number of coincidences which are recorded in 4 minutes are plotted as ordinates. Because of statistical fluctuations Ehmert attached no significance to the fact that the upper end the curve seems to show a drop of intensity, but one could be tempted to interpret the figure as showing a maximum of meson intensity at about 50 mm. Hg. Euler and Heisenberg (E 7) predicted such a maximum at about 80 mm. Hg., but under an assumption, which has recently been thrown into doubt (cf. sect. 3), that the mesons originate from the light quanta of the soft component, which, according to the Yukawa theory, can excite one or several mesons by impact with a heavy particle (neutron, proton) (Wentzel (W 4) and Heitler (H 6)).

Corresponding experiments were made by Schein, Jesse, and Wollan.

They used the arrangement of counter tubes sketched in Fig. 2 in balloon flights up to 20 mm. Hg. The curve A (Fig. 2) shows the results of measurements with various lead absorbers (dashed), which varied between 4 and 18 cm. in thickness. In all cases, in contradiction to an earlier measure-

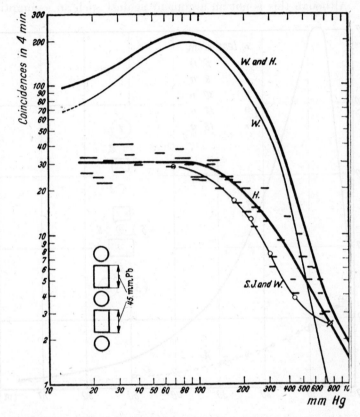

Fig. 1. The number "H" of particles penetrating 9 cm of lead as a function of atmospheric pressure as measured by EHMERT (E 2) with the countertube arrangement sketched in the lower left. The circles and "S. J & W" give the measurements of SCHEIN, JESSE, and WALLAN (S 5) with 8 cms of lead. "W & H" shows the variation of the total vertical radiation according to PFOTZER (P 2, 3). "W" is the difference of the curves "W & H" and "H" which at the same time agrees with the variation of the shower frequency according to REGNER and EHMERT (R 2).

ment by the same authors, the meson intensity increased up to the greatest height reached, and no indication of a flattening off or of a maximum appeared. These authors further established the fact that there were no electrons of such intensity that they could have penetrated the lead and simulated the hard rays by shower formation. At least, it is evident from the close agreement of the points obtained with different thicknesses of lead that electrons did not influence these measurements. We will come back to this point in the next section.

One may say that the experiments have, thus far, not confirmed the expectation that the meson intensity falls off again at the top of the atmosphere. Although this is not an argument against such an assumption, it

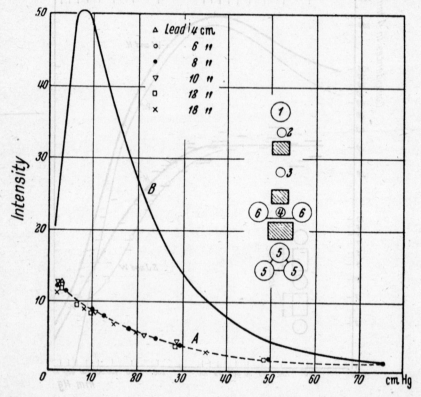

Figure 2. Measurements of SCHEIN, JESSE and WOLLAN (S 5). Curve A: Intensity of the hard component for various thicknesses of lead as a function of pressure in cm Hg. Curve B: Total intensity of cosmic rays according to PFOTZER (P 2, 3).

does mean that the mesons apparently are not generated from the soft component alone, as Euler and Heisenberg assumed, but are excited at the very top of the atmosphere by primary particles, which are very rapidly absorbed in the atmosphere.

3. Protons as Primaries

a) **Work of Schein, Jesse and Wollan.** In the work cited above Schein, Jesse, and Wollan (S 5) have obtained results which are of great significance in our understanding of the creation of mesons. Previously, as mentioned above, one started out in the discussion of meson creation with the assumption (Euler, Heisenberg) that they are excited high in the atmosphere by the light quanta of the very intense soft component, and thus predominantly in the region of the maximum of the Pfotzer curve. For this there were various arguments.

The excitation of mesons by light quanta is a possible process according to the Yukawa theory. For these mesons one assumed a spectrum similar to that of the exciting light quanta of the soft component. The latter was believed to be known accurately since the observed total intensity of the cosmic rays could be understood on the shower theory if one postulated a corresponding spectrum of electrons as the primary radiation incident from external space. The so-conceived meson spectrum was supported by the facts that it was in relatively good agreement with Blackett's measurements of the meson spectrum and that the same spectrum also occurred in the distribution of large bursts under thick absorbers. This interpretation was given by Euler and Heisenberg.

Schein, Jesse, and Wollan (S 4) have found an indication that mesons are also created by the light quanta of the cascade radiation. With a coincidence arrangement consisting of four counters, in which the upper tube was not shielded, and the lower ones were separated by a total of 10 cms. of lead, it was shown that there are rays which pass through the upper tube without ionization and then apparently they excite hard particles in the lead. The frequency of these rays varies with the height about like the intensity of the soft component. (cf. Sect. 5 of this Chapter).

From the postulate that the mesons are all created by the cascade radiation, it would follow that, at the height where the energetic mesons constituting the penetrating radiation (a few 10^9eV) at sea level should be excited, there must also be electrons and positrons of comparable intensity and energy, as well as the light quanta and mesons. A proof of this point was undertaken by Schein, Jesse, and Wollan (S 5) in the previously mentioned work. Electrons of these energies in passing through lead would be expected to release showers in the first counter tube with high probability. They tried to demonstrate the existence of these showers. In the arrangement sketched in Fig. 2 the counter tubes 1, 2, 3, 4 and 2, 3, 4, 5 registered the vertical intensity for 4 and 6 cms. of lead respectively; the counter tubes 1, 2, 6, 4 and 2, 6, 4, 5 registered particles which were accompanied by showers. In no case was more than a small percentage of the measured penetrating particles accompanied by showers in the side tubes. This result is in contradiction to the hypothesis that the energetic mesons are created by the soft component. The authors make the following remarks on their observations:

"From the uniform hardness of the particles measured, as indicated by curve A (Fig. 2), and from the fact that they excite no showers, we conclude that there are no electrons of energy between 10^9 and 10^{12} eV in the highest altitudes reached. Since the energy which an electron needs to penetrate the earth's magnetic field at the 51° geomagnetic latitude of the experiments is about $3 \cdot 10^9$ eV, and since our measurements were carried out within the first radiation unit (i.e. the distance in which an electron or light quantum makes one multiplication according to the cascade theory) from the top of the atmosphere, it seems difficult to postulate the existence of electrons of energy $E < 10^{12}$ eV, in the primary cosmic rays. They must, therefore, consist of some other kind of penetrating charged particle. The mesons themselves, because of their spontaneous decay, cannot be the primary rays. It is therefore probable that the incident cosmic rays consist of protons." In regard to this result of the experiments of Schein, Jesse, and Wollan, one must remark that in spite of all of the evidence submitted favoring the creation of mesons from the cascade rays there is no agreement as to their primaries.

We have already seen that the relatively small latitude effect of the hard component at sea level becomes compatible with the hypothesis of their creation by the cascades if it is admitted that more than 85% are created by primaries of such energy that they are not influenced by the earth's field. On the other hand, on exactly the same grounds, the possibility has been left open that at least a part of the mesons are created from other unidentified primary components. In the case of the field sensitive rays there is definite evidence for other than electron primaries as we will see in what follows:

b) **Work of Johnson.** As early as the year 1934 Johnson (J 7) working at an altitude of 45 cm. Hg. established that showers of the soft component possess an asymmetry of less than 1%. At the same time it was known that the soft rays show a latitude effect which proves that their primaries in any case are charged. From this it must be concluded on the basis of the cascade theory and the maintenance of direction deducible from it (cf. Chapt. 3, Molière) that these primaries are made up of positive and negative particles in approximately equal numbers. The total intensity of the cosmic rays at sea level, for which the hard component is mainly responsible, has an east-west asymmetry of some 15% and shows that the field sensitive primaries must consist almost exclusively of positive particles. This conclusion follows from a quantitative comparison (Johnson (J 9)) of the east-west asymmetry with the latitude effect of the hard radiation and concerns, therefore, only the small part of the hard rays which are latitude sensitive. These primaries, therefore, must not be identical with those of the soft radiation. Johnson suggested that they probably consist of protons. This postulate, which seems confirmed by the new investigations of Schein, Jesse, and Wollan, had, therefore, been announced much earlier. There remains, nevertheless, the question of how the contemporary opinion that all primaries, including those of the soft component, are protons, is to be reconciled with Johnson's view that the primary radiation of this component consists of positive and negative particles. Johnson's theory is based upon the failure of the cascades to show an east-west effect. Before we go into this question we will describe, in detail, a new work by Johnson and Barry (J 13), which confirms and extends his earlier work.

Here Johnson investigated the east-west effect of the total radiation 20° north of the equator and at a great height. Three counter tubes in coincidence collimated a beam angle of 20°. Moreover, this beam direction was inclined 60° with respect to the zenith. The counter arrangement was sent with balloons to a height of some 30 mm. Hg. The investigations were made close to the magnetic equator because there the east-west asymmetry should be especially great. The coincidences, as well as the orientation of the balloon with respect to the sun, registered by means of a photocell, were transmitted to a ground station by radio. The results of four flights are given in the table.

Altitude mm Hg	East			West			α
	Number coincidences	Time Min.	Coincidences per Min.	Number coincidences	Time Min.	Coincidences per Min.	
29.4	1100	28.3	38.9	1523	35.4	43	0.1
33	277	10.5	26.3	413	14.9	27.6	0.048
44	464	18.5	25.1	680	24.6	27.6	0.095
24.2	554	19.3	28.7	740	23.8	31.1	0.08

Average: 0.072

$$\alpha = \frac{2(j_w - j_\bullet)}{j_w + j_\bullet} = 0.072.$$

Therefore, about 7% more rays come from the west than from the east. This result, which applies to the total radiation composed of both the hard and the soft components, was analysed by Johnson in the following manner:

The latitude effect of the soft and of the total radiation is known from the balloon measurements of Bowen, Millikan, and Neher (B 34). From their curves of total ionization as a function of the atmospheric depth and with the help of a transformation given by Gross (G 11), (also Johnson (J 9)) Johnson derives the intensity of the radiation at the height reached by him and at a 60° zenith angle, on the assumption that the intensity at zenith angle Θ depends upon $h/\cos \Theta$, where h is the equivalent thickness of the atmosphere above the counter tubes, expressed in mm. of Hg. The lower energy limit of the incident rays at 20° north latitude ($15 \cdot 10^9$eV) can be determined from the Lemaitre-Vallarta theory (Chapt. 15, Meixner). From this lower limit one can further compute, according to Lemaitre-Vallarta, the variation of the total intensity which would take place in turning the coincidence telescope 360° in azimuth at zenith angle 60°, if one assumes, for example, that all primaries are positive. In this case the asymmetry between east and west would amount to some 60% or about 10 times that observed.

Since this discussion is based on the latitude effect, Johnson concludes that in reality only a small excess of positives over negatives is present. On the other hand, since present day arguments seem to deny the validity of this interpretation, one could interpret Johnson's results as indicating that the coupling between the directions of primaries and those of the secondaries which constitute the cascades is not as close as had previously been assumed and for this reason the east-west effect is lacking. One can understand such a state of affairs on the supposition that the Pfotzer maximum consists of particles of low energy, as is confirmed by the measurements of Schein, Jesse, and Wollan, and that, in consequence, the change of direction of electrons in scattering is so great that the primary direction is no longer preserved; alternatively, it may well be that, in the still unknown process of the creation of cascades from the primaries, the primary directions become confused.

Johnson concluded from the 7% asymmetry that the part of the intensity which is excited by excess positive radiation makes up some 12% of the total field sensitive radiation, and from this he estimated on the basis of his observed east-west asymmetries at sea level that it was to be ascribed in part, if not altogether, to the hard radiation. Johnson also assumed that the primaries of this part of the radiation were positive and most probably protons. The views of Johnson were supported by investigations by Jones (J 14) and Hughes (H 13). They observed meson tracks in the Wilson chamber placed in a magnetic field. Jones found 29% more positive mesons in the range from 0.2 to $10 \cdot 10^9$eV. Hughes, in the same institution, observed about a 20% excess of positives in the same energy range. A frequency maximum of mesons was also observed at from 1 to $2 \cdot 10^9$eV. (Compare in this connection the medium altitude investigations described in Sect. 5).

Johnson's results did not quite suffice to lend certainty to the proton hypothesis. A related experiment which should provide the missing support would be to measure the east-west effect of the hard component alone at great heights, where such an effect must be very pronounced.[1]

TRANSLATOR'S NOTE: The German edition through some misunderstanding of the author carries the footnote "This experiment was carried out in very recent times by

Moreover, the picture which resulted from Johnson's work was not free from contradictions in regard to the formation of cascades from primary electrons. Thus, Nordheim (cf. Johnson and Barry (J 13)) remarked that one must conclude from Johnson's measurements that the cascades as well must be produced in part by an excess of positive primaries. Johnson had assumed that the asymmetry of 7% observed at about 30—40 mm. could arise from the hard component alone, which then would have to be excited entirely by positive primaries, for example, by protons. On the other hand, Nordheim argued that, at this height and at this angle of inclination of the coincidence telescope, the soft component, according to the cascade theory, should have multiplied to about 30 times the number of primary particles, while the hard component, on the contrary, should not have multiplied at all. Since the total number of hard rays at this altitude is about 10% of the total radiation, the total number of primaries of the hard rays would have to be three times as great as that of the soft primaries. In reality, according to present views, the total energy, and hence the total number of rays of the hard component, is not more than 10% of the total radiation. From this Nordheim concluded that either the asymmetry is false, or the hard component experiences a strong multiplication, or, what is most probable, the greater part of the asymmetry results from the soft radiations.

If one would conclude on the basis of the results of Schein, Jesse, and Wollan, as well as those of Johnson, that protons are the only primaries of the total cosmic radiation, then it would be interesting to look for protons in the cosmic rays at great heights; it is known that they are rare at sea level and in medium heights.

Finally, it may be remarked that Swann has independently concluded from his observations that the primaries of the cosmic rays can not be electrons but are probably protons. In several stratosphere flights Swann has observed that the ratio of vertical to horizontal total intensity deviates appreciably from that to be expected for primary electrons. Thus, at a height of 15 cm. Hg., the horizontal intensity is 20%, and at 4 cm. it is 80% of the vertical, whereas for the latter value, for example, one would expect 17% if the effective height of the traversed atmospheric layer at a telescope inclination Θ is to be taken as $h/\cos \Theta$. Swann concludes from this that the primaries excite the secondaries in such a manner that they lose their original directions. Therefore the primaries can not be electrons on the basis of the cascade theory.

SCHEIN and associates (transmitted by letter). In fact there was found a pronounced east-west effect of the hard rays which showed that the total hard component arises from positive primaries." However SCHEIN states that he neither performed this experiment nor wrote such a letter. In (S 5) SCHEIN, JESSE and WOLLAN propose this experiment.

If one assumes protons as the primaries, then Swann's findings have an analogy in the previously cited absence of the east-west effect of the soft component at great heights and should have the same explanation.

4. Excitation of High Energy Mesons in Multiple Processes

One of the first analyses of experimental results which led to the view that several energetic mesons are excited by a single primary particle was carried out by Nordheim and Hebb (N 9) and by Nordheim (N 8). The main part of their work consisted of a quantitative consideration of meson production from the soft component under the hypothesis that the latter was created from a primary electron component in accordance with the cascade theory. In this they were led to assume the creation of perhaps 3 or 4 mesons in one act. In addition, Nordheim discussed the possibility that, in addition to the primary electron spectrum which excites the cascades, there is also a primary proton component which excites the mesons. For this case also he had to assume a high multiplicity of meson formation.

In the preceding section it is assumed that both components are excited by a single primary proton radiation. If this concept is correct, the hypothesis of the Nordheim-Hebb work must undergo alteration. On the other hand the essential features of their deductions remain undisturbed: some 80% of the mesons at sea level have an energy of about $2 \cdot 10^9 eV$ or less (Hughes (H 13)). Since about $2 \cdot 10^9 eV$ is required to traverse the atmosphere, these rays must have at creation about $4 \cdot 10^9 eV$. If they were produced by primaries of this energy, there would be a latitude effect of 100%. If they were to be created by light-quanta of approximately the same energy, which, in turn, are secondaries of a primary radiation, then the primaries would have to have a higher energy, but there would still result a latitude effect of 40% to 50%. Since the latitude effect amounts to only 12% most of the primaries must therefore possess energies of more than $10^{10} eV$, and from the known intensity of primaries in this energy range it can be concluded that more than one meson must be created from a single primary.

Here there are two possibilities; either the mesons are created in a single act, or they are created one after the other. We will see later that the former is the more probable.

If, in the sense of the foregoing concept of meson production, light quanta are regarded as primaries, then the effective cross section for meson production in multiple processes can be evaluated according to Nordheim and Hebb (N 9). We will elucidate this theory in the interest of completeness. If one assumes about $1.5 \cdot 10^{10} eV$, as the energy of the exciting light quantum, then the multiplicity is 3 to 4. According to Compton and

Turner (C 7), the frequency of incidence of hard rays in the range of energies of $15 \cdot 10^9$eV is about $1.5 \cdot 10^{-4}$ rays per unit solid angle per sq. cm. per sec. in an energy interval of $1 \cdot 10^9$eV. From the shower theory (Chapt. 2, Heisenberg) one can deduce how many "photon lengths" $Q(E_0, k_0)$ (= path of a light quanta before a pair is excited) there are with an energy $> k_0$, originating in electrons with energy $< E_0$, and thus calculate the number of photon lengths for each energy interval of $1 \cdot 10^9$eV:

$$\frac{dQ}{dE_0} = 0.024 \cdot \left(\frac{1}{k_0} - \frac{1}{E_0}\right).$$

From this we can evaluate the ratio of mesons, created with a multiplicity r, to primary light quanta:

$$W_{(k)} = \frac{1.5 \cdot 10^4}{0.024 \cdot r \cdot \left(\frac{1}{\epsilon r} - \frac{1}{E_0}\right)} = \begin{cases} 1/50 \text{ for } r = 3 \\ 1/80 \text{ for } r = 4 \end{cases}$$

($\epsilon r = k_0$; ϵ = energy of created meson). This ratio is not entirely constant between $E_0 = 8$ and $E_0 = 15 \cdot 10^9$eV. It follows that the effective cross section is 1/50 to 1/80 of the known cross section for the excitation of pairs from light quanta (Chapt. 2, Flügge), i.e., between 0.5 and 1.10^{-27} cm.^{2} per nuclear particle. Schein, Jesse, and Wollan (S 4) (cf. Section 2) have determined the same cross-section as having the value $0.7 \cdot 10^{-27}$ cm.^{2}, but without considering the multiplicity.

An essentially higher effective cross section for meson excitation is obtained for energies $E_0 > 18 \cdot 10^9$eV on the basis of Wilson's observations (W 13) regarding the dependence of meson intensity on the amount of water traversed. The number of mesons observed by him with an energy between E and $E + dE$ is:

$$M(E)dE = 0.14 \frac{dE}{E^{2.8}} \quad \text{for } E > 6 \cdot 10^9 \text{eV.}[1]$$

This can again be compared with the frequency, deduced from the cascade theory, of photon lengths X_k of energy between k and $k + dk$.

$$X_k = 2 \cdot 65 \frac{dk}{k^{2.8}} \quad \text{for } k > 18 \cdot 10^9 \text{eV.}$$

For every 19 photon lengths one finds one meson of the same energy. Assuming that the multiplicity is about 3 and that the photon energy is

[1]NORDHEIM assumes a more rapid decrease of the spectrum for $E > 6 \cdot 10^{10}$eV on the basis of the stronger absorption at great water depths. This stronger absorption, however, probably has another cause. (cf. Chapt. 6, VOLTZ).

approximately equally distributed over the r mesons, then one obtains for the probability of such a process about 1/8 per photon length, i.e., about a 10 times larger value for the effective cross section than that for the mesons of low energy.

Nordheim saw a difficulty in his conception of meson excitation in multiple processes in the fact that the frequency of the inverse process should be of an equal order of magnitude. For this, however, the mesons have far too great a penetrating power. But in this connection it is to be borne in mind that for the multiple process the probability of the reverse reaction would be very small on account of the mesons running away from each other. The effective cross section for the reverse reaction would then be of the order of magnitude of the creation only when 2 mesons should accidentally meet simultaneously in a single collision; this is extremely improbable. The fact that the effective cross section for a single process like that of the absorption of a meson, is so small (smaller than that for the excitation by a factor of 10—100, Nordheim) can be taken as an argument for the belief that the *creation* of a *single* meson of very high energy must have a very small cross section and should take place rarely compared with the multiple process. This manner of argument applies not only to the creation of mesons from light quanta but gives general support to the concept of the creation of mesons in multiple processes.

Schein, Jesse, and Wollan (S 6) have tried to present experimental arguments that the mesons are created in multiple processes from the primary protons. For this purpose 4 groups of 4-fold coincidence counters were sent to great heights by balloons. The first two groups were used to count the vertical rays which could penetrate 18 cms. of lead. The third group counted two or more particles which appeared simultaneously with the penetrating particle after the first 4 cm. of lead (therefore, soft cascade particles) and the fourth group counted events in which one or more particles penetrated all of the lead simultaneously with the vertical particle. At heights of 3 cm. Hg. 46% of all hard rays excited coincidences in the fourth group and only 15% in the third group. From this result it follows that at least 85% of the mesons are created not in cascades. The large group of coincidences (46%) in the fourth group can best be explained by the assumption that a penetrating particle, probably a proton, excites a number of mesons in lead.

In this experiment we also have the proof of the creation of meson showers at great heights. Such showers with penetrating particles have been observed by various authors. Since references to these works are collected in Chapt. 5 (Klemm and Heisenberg), they may be skipped here. It is noteworthy that independently of the work of Schein, Jesse, and Wollan (S 5) Janossy (J 2), on the basis of his observations on the hard showers, has discussed the possibility of the excitation of the total cosmic radiation by a primary proton component.

There have also been preliminary theoretical discussions of the creation of cosmic rays by primary protons. Thus Swann (S 28) as well as Nordheim have evaluated the multiplicity of meson excitation from the latitude effect and obtained $r \sim 5$. Swann also gives a relation for the frequency of mesons of a given energy as a function of the depth below their point of creation. If a meson spectrum at the point of creation is assumed with an exponent -3 (cf. Chapt. 1, Heisenberg), and if, in addition, a life-period of $2 \cdot 10^{-6}$ sec. is ascribed to the mesons (cf. Chapt. 8, Heinsenberg), then Swann is able to represent correctly in rough detail the latitude effect and its dependence on the height.

5. Excitation of Slow Mesons from the Soft Component

Schein, Wollan, and Groetzinger (S 8) have investigated the meson radiation at heights up to 9.3 km. with the help of coincidence counters in airplanes. They come to the result that a part of the mesons observed by them are excited by neutral primaries which are probably not photons, and in addition they obtain a surprising spectrum of the mesons at this height. Their results are here briefly described. In Fig. 3 the coincidence arrangement is reproduced. The coincidences set off by ionizing particles are independently registered in the counter tubes 1, 2, 3, 4 and 2, 3, 4, 5 as well as 1, 2, 3, 4, 5. Coincidences from sidewise showers are ruled out to within a few percent. They find for example, with an airplane between 5.2 and 7.4 km. height the following result: Of the particles which excite the upper 4 counter tubes $22 \pm 3\%$ do not discharge counter tube No. 5; of those which excite the lower 4 counter tubes $9.7 \pm 3\%$ do not discharge counter tube No. 1; there are, accordingly, 12% more counts above than below. The result for the lower group, which seems to be independent of the height, means, according to the interpretation of the authors, that a neutral particle passes through 6 cms. of lead and counter No. 1, and then, in the 8 cms. thick lead block, it excites an ionizing hard particle, a meson. If the neutral particle were a light quantum of such high energy that it could pass through 6 cms. of lead, then, according to the views of the author, it would be expected that in its absorption it would also create an electron which would excite the first counter. It is inferred that the mesons are not created by photons.

In this connection there is perhaps also the possibility that a sidewise light quantum strikes the lead block over the second counter tube and there excites a meson which discharges the tubes 2 to 4. In the excitation of mesons the secondaries often deviate from the primary direction by a

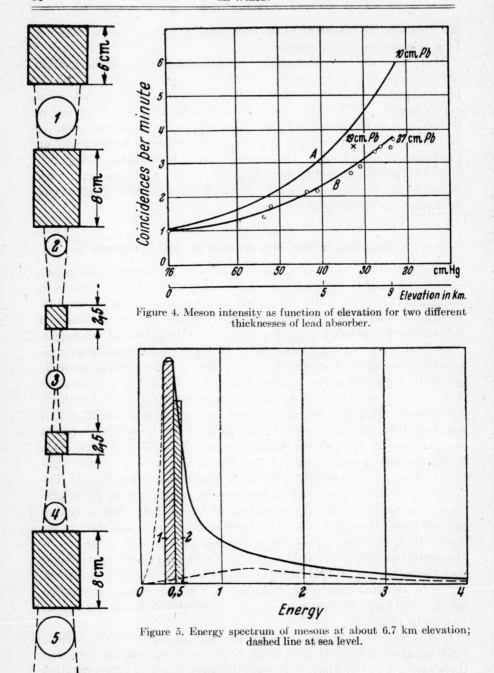

Figure 4. Meson intensity as function of elevation for two different
thicknesses of lead absorber.

Figure 5. Energy spectrum of mesons at about 6.7 km elevation;
dashed line at sea level.

Figure 3. Arrangement of counter tubes in the
work of SCHEIN, WOLLAN and GROETZINGER (S 8).

considerable amount, according to the evidence of the Wilson chamber. The supposition that mesons are also excited in thin lead plates by photons has been made probable by Schein and his associates; we will describe these investigations next.   In a special series of measurements they attempted to show that in the primaries there are no effects attributable to neutrons. For these experiments a parafin block of 35 cm. thickness was laid over the arrangement of counters.   If neutrons of higher energy had been present they would have effected an appreciable increase in the coincidence rate because of the recoil protons.   Such an increase did not occur within the 4% limit of error of the measurements.   The only remaining possibility is that the mesons are excited by neutral mesons or neutrinos.

Very similar experiments were carried out by Rossi and Regener (R 10) at 4.5 km. height.   They also found a considerable number of mesons which were excited by neutral particles after passing through lead.   They could effect a decrease in the mesons thus excited by increasing the lead thickness, but this was less than would have been expected from the absorption of mesons.

Neutral mesons were also discussed on the basis of similar observations by Maas (M 2), who postulated photons as primaries, and by Arley and Heitler (A 6), since the absorption effect for the primaries, observed by Maas, agreed with that for the mesons.

From the results already described of Schein, Wollan, and Groetzinger, it is possible to draw conclusions regarding the spectrum of the mesons at the altitudes attained.   From the investigations the intensity of the meson radiation which was able to pass through 27 cms. of lead (cf. Fig. 3) was found to vary with the height in the manner shown by curve B of Fig. 4. Likewise the corresponding intensity curve was taken with only 10 cms. of lead.   (Fig. 4 Curve A).   A single point ($\times$) gives the number of mesons at 6.7 km. altitude which can penetrate 19 cms. of lead.   This point was determined from the coincidences of the upper counter tubes between 5.2 and 7.4 km.   The difference between curves A and B can be due only to the mesons which pass through 10 cms. of lead but are stopped in the additional 17 cms.   On the basis of the known intensity loss of mesons in lead (Wilson (W 15)), it follows that a meson requires an energy of $2.9 \cdot 10^8$ or $5.2 \cdot 10^8$ eV in order to penetrate 10 cms. or 27 cms. of lead, respectively.   The difference between the ordinates of curves A and B gives the number of mesons which lie between these two values.   For 9.3 km. altitude this is about 1/3 of all observed mesons.   For the penetration of 10 cms. of lead $4.2 \cdot 10^8$ eV is necessary.   Hughes (H 13) obtained data from Wilson chamber photographs at sea level for mesons $> 5 \cdot 10^9$ eV; Herzog, and Herzog and Bostik (H 7, 8, 9) using an airplane found results which we will presently describe.   Making use of all these data Schein, Wollan, and Groetzinger construct the meson spectrum at 6.7 km. height which is reproduced in Fig. 5 and is there compared with the well known spectrum at sea level (Hughes (H 13), Jones (J 14), Blackett (B 22)) represented by the dashed line. From the constancy of the meson absorption above 6 km. height (Schein, Jesse, Wollan (S 4)) these authors conclude that the spectrum should undergo no further essential alterations at greater heights.

The large number of mesons with energy $< 5.2 \cdot 10^8$eV was confirmed, as already stated, by Wilson chamber photographs by Herzog and Bostik (H 7, 8, 9), who have likewise found about 30% slow mesons at the same height. From their photographs it appears, without doubt, that these mesons are created in part by multiple processes in the neighborhood of the chamber; the creation of one pair in the chamber was photographed. These mesons should, therefore, have been produced is some manner other than that of the energetic mesons described in the preceding section. They are probably formed from the photons of the soft radiation. An argument for this view is also given by the investigations of Schein, Jesse, and Wollan mentioned at the beginning of section 3; they studied the intensity of a non-ionizing radiation, at various heights, which excites mesons in 2 cms. of lead. Its intensity increases with the height in the same way as the cascade radiation measured by Regener and Ehmert (R 2). From these measurements Schein and Wilson (S 7) have evaluated the effective cross section for the excitation of these mesons. From the measurements of Regener and Ehmert it follows that at a height of 8 km. about 100 photons must fall each second on the 2 cm. thick lead screen of the counter tube arrangement. In the same time 2 mesons were observed. Hence the probability for excitation is 2/100. From the number of lead atoms per cc. the authors calculate from this number that the effective cross section per nuclear particle in lead is $0.7 \cdot 10^{-27}$ cm.^{2} Nordheim and Hebb (N 9) have shown from the frequency of energetic mesons at great heights that the effective cross section for excitation of energetic mesons must be at least 10 times greater if one assumes that photons of the cascades are the primaries. This result also leads to the conclusion that there is probably another mechanism of excitation at the edge of the atmosphere.

6. Summary

The experimental investigations make it appear that the following picture for the creation of mesons is the most probable:

From external space there is incident, according to Johnson, a primary proton radiation whose energy spectrum probably agrees with that found for the soft component and for the mesons. (cf. Chapt. 1, Heisenberg). The protons excite the hard meson component, probably in multiple processes, at the outer bounds of the atmosphere, i.e., in a path length which is shorter than a radiation length. The soft radiation which forms the Pfotzer maximum is created in the same or in a separate act from the primary, or it is a secondary radiation of the mesons. Experimentally nothing is known of this. The mesons form the hard component of the cosmic radiation which is observed at sea level and has a frequency maximum at that depth at $2 \cdot 10^9 eV$. Mesons are also produced in another manner, and probably in great numbers, as secondaries of photons of the soft component, but with less energy ($< 5.2 \cdot 10^8 eV$). Here also multiple processes (explosions) are observed. In the vicinity of the earth's surface these mesons are very rare, in agreement with the fact that there also the soft cascade radiation has been almost completely absorbed. At 7 km. height, on the contrary, these make up about 30% of the total meson component. Besides those from the photons, probably a small fraction ($< 5\%$) of the mesons are created by neutral corpuscular particles (possibly neutral mesons). Future investigations must be undertaken to show in what manner the mesons and cascade radiation arise from the primaries and how the geomagnetic effect and the intensity relationships are to be explained.

5. SHOWERS WITH PENETRATING PARTICLES

By A. KLEMM and W. HEISENBERG, Berlin-Dahlem

The question arises whether showers containing several penetrating particles are also observed in the cosmic radiation. This is, theoretically, of fundamental significance, since from the presence of such showers one might come to some conclusion about the existence of genuine multiple processes (or explosions) in which several particles are created in a single act. This type of explosion-like shower is to be expected, theoretically, according to the Yukawa theory (cf. W. Heisenberg (H 3); also Chapt. 8, Heisenberg). A distinction is to be made between the genuine showers and the pairs of penetrating particles which are occasionally counted in with the showers. In what follows the word "shower" will be applied only to processes with at least 3 particles; the discussion of pairs will be dealt with briefly.

1. Meson Pairs

The first indication of pairs of penetrating particles resulted from investigations by Maas (M 1) and by Schmeizer and Bothe (B 30a, S 9). The latter authors investigated coincidences of counters at a great distance from a shower-exciting layer and under such a condition found the so-called second maximum of the Rossi curve strongly marked at 17 cms. of lead. They came to the conclusion from this that rays exist with a range of 17 cms. of Pb. The various repetitions of this experiment undertaken with slightly varied geometry, however, have not led to a complete confirmation of the existence of the second maximum.

A more certain proof for the appearance of pairs of penetrating particles and, indeed of meson pairs, is supplied by the work of Braddick and Hensby (B 35), Leisegang (L 3) and Herzog and Bostick (B 8, 9).

Braddick and Hensby (B 35) have taken counter controlled cloud chamber pictures in London 30 m. underground. They obtained 1900 photographs with single meson tracks. The mesons were recognized by their uneventful passage through 1.4 cms. and 2.5 cms. of lead in succession. Of these 1900 photographs 5 showed double tracks of mesons with an apparently common source in the layer of earth above the chamber. With 1900 single tracks only 0.057 accidental double tracks were to be expected.

Leisegang (L 3) made counter controlled Wilson-photographs, in which 11 cms. and 16 cms. of lead in turn were placed above the chamber and a 1 cm. lead screen was in the chamber. Among 900 single meson tracks he found 3 double tracks, the origin of which was in the producing layer. The proof of their meson character was realized in that the particles were scarcely deflected in 1 cm. of lead (and were therefore energetic), and they produced no secondary rays.

Finally, Herzog and Bostick (H 8, 9) have observed the formation of a meson pair in a cloud chamber photograph taken at high altitude in an airplane.

Figure 1. Shower with penetrating particles observed by FUSSELL.

There can, therefore, no longer be any doubt that occasionally pairs of mesons are formed. It is plausible to assume that the primary particle is a photon, that we have here to deal with processes analogous to the usual pair excitation of electrons. The frequency of pairs can be evaluated from the available material only in order of magnitude. The effective cross section for their creation from protons seems to lie in the vicinity of 10^{-27} to 10^{-26} cm.^{2} per nuclear particle. This order of magnitude is also not out of the question according to theoretical evaluations (e.g. Booth and Wilson (B 29)).

2. Penetrating Showers

The proof of the appearance of genuine showers with penetrating particles was first given by Fussell (F 7) in some cloud chamber photographs, then by a systematic counter-tube investigation by Wataghin, Santos, and Pompeja (W 2) and also more thoroughly by Jánossy and Ingleby (J 3).

Fig. 1 shows the best example of such a process observed by Fussell. The shower took place in a 0.7 mm. thick lead plate. Of its rays at least 3 passed through 1.2 to 2 cms. of lead without appreciable deflection and without secondary formation, and are, therefore, to be regarded as mesons. The shower excitation is connected with a nuclear disruption, as is shown by the heavy tracks of short range. The whole shower took place simultaneously with electrons which did not come from the place of formation of the shower; the process, therefore, seems to have taken place in the area of a large air shower.

Wataghin, Santos and Pompeja (W 2), working at 800 m. above sea level, have placed four counter tubes of 100 cm.^{2} each so that in each pair the two counters are vertically under one another and the pairs are separated horizontally, 30 cms. in one case and 65 cms. in the other. A particle coming vertically from above and causing a pair of counter tubes to respond must penetrate 17 cms. of lead. The authors observed four-fold coincidences and found, with 30 cm. separation, 4.5 coincidences per day and, with 65 cm. separation, 3.6 coincidences per day, whereas they report that only 0.3 coincidences per day were to have been expected accidentally. Here they were evidently dealing with pairs of penetrating particles, most probably mesons. With a fifth counter-tube, placed there for the purpose, it was further established that in a considerable fraction of the cases more than two penetrating particles appeared since the five-fold coincidences were not much rarer than the four-fold.

The most thorough investigation of this type and the one most productive of conclusions was one carried out by Jánossy and Ingleby (J 3). They chose the arrangement of Fig. 2.

When a five fold coincidence occurred, 1, 2, 3, A, B the number, n, of

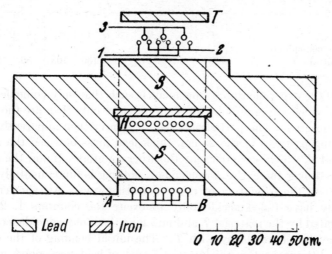

Figure 2. Experimental arrangement of JÁNOSSY and INGLEBY.

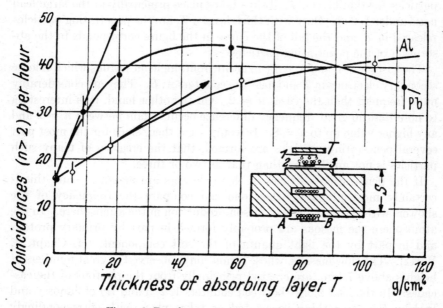

Figure 3. Development of penetrating showers.

simultaneously discharged H-counters was recorded. As an exciting layer T, both lead and Al were used, the thickness of this layer varying between 0 and 120 g/cm.[2] The absorbing layer S consisted of lead. The results may be seen in the following table and in Fig. 3.

	$n =$	0	1	2	3	4	5	6	7	8
Number of coincidences (for arbitrary T)		854	911	184	139	130	108	80	85	49

If $T = 0$ the experimental arrangement is such that only coincidences are observed which are excited by air showers, since only then are the upper 3 counters excited. The particles of the air shower then apparently release penetrating particles in the 25 cm. thick lead mass between the counters 1, 2, 3 and H, which serve to excite the other counters. If now the material T is placed over the entire arrangement, nothing is fundamentally altered in regard to the formation of the penetrating rays. Air showers which previously have failed accidentally to excite the counters 1, 2, 3, are concentrated by the material T and now give threefold coincidences 1, 2, 3; hence the rise of frequency with T. The initial bending of the curve in Fig. 3 and the saturation thickness at 5 cms. of lead correspond exactly to the relations expected from the cascade theory. The release of penetrating particles for thin layers, T, always takes place principally in the large lead mass under 1, 2, 3. Only with thick layers, T, are the penetrating particles released in T, and the fall of the curve in the figure corresponds to the absorption of the penetrating particles.

The cases $n = 0$ and $n = 1$ can occur from single mesotrons which release secondary electrons in T and near the counters A, B. They are considerably more frequent than the cases $n = 2$. On the other hand, it is interesting to note that no great frequency difference occurs again between $n = 2$ and any higher value up to $n = 8$. It would seem then, since for the most part several penetrating particles are formed, that the creation of many such particles is not much rarer than that of two or three.

If the penetrating particles of these showers are mesons, —and this is certainly most probable—then one can compare the frequency of the showers with the frequency of meson production in the atmosphere. In the atmosphere the mesons are probably formed in part by primary protons and in part by the light quanta of the soft component. (cf. Chapt. 4, Wirtz). The slow mesons, whose formation is observed in great numbers at heights above 7 km., are created principally from the photons of the cascades. In the lead block (between counters 1, 2, 3 and H) of Jánossy and Ingleby the same thing is enacted as takes place with correspondingly greater frequency at the higher altitudes. Hence, the frequency of the meson showers in these investigations can be extrapolated: they should be related to the frequency of single mesons in the same way as the cascade radiation of sea level is related to that at great heights. For a cascade spectrum of the form $E^{-1.8}$ the intensity at sea level, according to the theory, is 10^{-4} to 10^{-5} of that at greater heights. Hence the showers of Jánossy and Ingleby should be 10^5 times rarer than that of the single mesotrons, a ratio which is about of the right order of magnitude. This estimate, therefore, supports the interpretation that the investigations of Jánossy and Ingleby have to do with meson showers (i.e. genuine explosive showers in which many particles are created in a single act). The correctness of this interpretation can also be demonstrated by the dependence of the frequency upon the height. Even at the height of the Yungfraujoch the showers should be 80 times more frequent than at sea level.

Recently Powell (P 6) and Wollan (W 16) have published cloud chamber photographs in which showers of mesons have been observed emanating from a single point (Fig. 4). These showers are exactly the same kind as

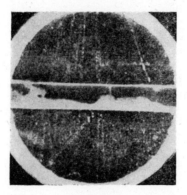

Figure 4. Meson shower by WOLLAN.

those observed (See Fig. 1) by Fussell (F 7). Whether the showers observed by Daudin (D 1) also belong to the same class can be clarified only by further experiments. Finally, Cocconi, Loverdo, and Tongiorgi (C 5a) have recently published systematic experiments, which show that most of the meson showers at 2200 m. are created in connection with the large air showers. These results, therefore, are in good agreement with those obtained by Jánossy and Ingleby.

In summary it can be stated: by experiments conducted in the past few years one can be sure of the existence of explosive meson showers with many particles; these showers seem to play a decisive roll in the genetics of the cosmic rays in the atmosphere according to the new experiments by Schein, Jesse, and Wollan (S 4 to 6) (cf. Chapt. 4, Wirtz). This experimental result is satisfying because such showers are to be expected according to the Yukawa theory, (Heisenberg (H 3)); the existence of these showers also gives a theoretical basis to explain why the effective cross section for collision or creation process of the mesons, calculated according to the usual perturbation theory, does not agree with the experiments. Only in the kind of calculation which has to do with the purely electromagnetic effect of the meson on its surroundings can one hope to get an agreement with the experiments.

6. THE ABSORPTION OF MESONS

By H. Voltz, Berlin-Charlottenburg

As we know from measurements by Anderson and Neddermeyer (A 4) as well as those by Blackett (B 24), the great penetrating power of the cosmic rays is a property of the mesons which they contain. These particles, thus far found only in the cosmic rays, should be unstable according to the theory of Yukawa, who, theoretically, postulated particles of such mass before their discovery to explain β-decay and nuclear forces; they should decay into an electron and a neutrino with a mean life of the order of 10^{-6} sec.

Such a decay of the mesons, like the normal absorption by energy loss, will lead to a reduction in the number of particles while passing through matter; the measured absorption coefficient will, therefore, contain, besides the part due to collision losses, another part attributable to the decay. In what follows the absorption of mesons due to collision losses alone will be considered, and, in conclusion, the question will be raised as to what can be determined from the experiments about the decay of the mesons.

The collision losses of mesons take place essentially by energy transfers to the electrons, or in other words, by the ionization of the atoms encountered[1]. For the energy losses suffered in this process, Bohr (B 28) has derived, on classical theoretical grounds, an expression which was later brought into quantum mechanical form by Bloch (B 26). According to his theory

$$-\left(\frac{dE}{dx}\right) = \frac{2\pi n e^4}{mv^2}\left\{\log\frac{mv^2 W}{I^2 Z^2} - \log\left(1 - \frac{v^2}{c^2}\right) + \left(1 - \frac{v^2}{c^2}\right)\right\}. \tag{1}$$

Here e and m stand for the charge and mass of the electron, v the velocity of the moving particle, n the number of electrons per cc. in the material traversed, IZ (with $I = 13.5$ eV) a mean value of the ionization energy of an atom of atomic number Z, and W the maximum energy which can be transferred to an electron in a collision. According to Bhabha (B 19)

$$W = \frac{(E^2 - M^2 c^4)}{Mc^2\left(\dfrac{m}{2M} + \dfrac{M}{2m} + \dfrac{E}{Mc^2}\right)}, \tag{2}$$

---

[1]To what extent radiation losses play a part with energies above 10^{10}eV is still not fully understood.

in which M stands for the mass of the meson.—According to (1) the energy loss, besides depending upon the velocity of the particles, depends essentially upon the number of electrons encountered, or in other words, roughly speaking, upon the mass of the layer traversed. There is also a logarithmic dependence upon the atomic number of the absorbing medium.

Numerous experimental investigations (Rossi (R 6)) now show that the absorption of mesons in air is appreciably stronger than in a water medium, which, according to (1), would give the same energy loss. This phenomenon has been regarded as an experimental proof of the decay of mesons. This decay must, naturally, have a greater effect over the long path length through a gaseous absorber than on the short path through a liquid or solid absorber and, hence, must lead to a higher absorption effect of air. From the experiments it was possible to determine the mean life as a few times 10^{-6} seconds, so that the Yukawa theory could be regarded as confirmed in its basic concepts.

Fermi (F 1) has recently pointed out in this regard that this conclusion is not entirely inevitable. Indeed, the derivation of the collision-loss formula (1), neglects an effect which makes the normal absorption by energy loss, even of a stable particle, depend upon the density of the absorbing medium. This is just what the experiments show i.e., that a liquid or solid absorber produces a lower loss of energy than a gaseous absorber. This effect arises from the fact that in the material traversed the electric field of the passing particle induces a polarization which weakens the ionizing field. In this way the energy loss of the particle is reduced, and the more so, the greater the dielectric constant, i.e., the greater the density of the absorbing material.

Before one can draw conclusions from the experiments as to the instability of the mesons, the influence of the above effect must be determined quantitatively. The calculation, of which the essential result is to be presented briefly in what follows, was carried through by Fermi and leads to the conclusion that one must still, as before, adhere to the assumption of the spontaneous decay of mesons. However, one arrives at a higher value of the mean life than previously.

For the calculation Fermi replaces the matter traversed by a continuum of electrons elastically bound to their rest positions and calculates for this model the electric and magnetic field of the moving particle. With the help of the radiation vector one obtains the energy flux which passes outwards through a cylindrical surface circumscribed about the orbit with a radius b. This represents the energy lost per second to the region outside of the cylinder and can be compared immediately with the corresponding expression of the Bohr theory, which is derived without regard to the dielectric properties of the medium. It shows, however, in contradiction to the latter, a dependence upon the density of the material.

Without the calculation losing sense, the radius of the cylinder can be reduced to the order of magnitude of an atom radius. Then, moreover, one can regard the energy lost to the region inside the cylinder as independent of the dielectric properties of the cylinder and simply add the difference found in the above calculation with respect to the Bohr expression for the region outside of the cylinder to the formula (1) which gives the old value for energy loss.

In the calculation two cases are to be distinguished according as $v < c/(\epsilon)^{\frac{1}{2}}$ or $v > c/(\epsilon)^{\frac{1}{2}}$. Here ϵ is the corresponding static dielectric constant of the assumed model: $\epsilon = 1 + 4\pi n e^2/m\omega_0^2$, where ω_0 stands for the characteristic frequency of the electrons. If the evaporation of electrons is neglected, one obtains for the energy loss to the region outside the cylinder of radius b per cm. of the path traversed by the particle.

$$
\left.\begin{aligned}
-\left(\frac{dE}{dx}\right)_b &= \frac{2\pi n e^4}{mv^2}\left\{\frac{2b\omega_0(\epsilon)^{\frac{1}{2}}}{v}K_0\left(\frac{b\omega_0(\epsilon)^{\frac{1}{2}}}{v}\right)K_1\left(\frac{b\omega_0(\epsilon)^{\frac{1}{2}}}{v}\right)\right. \\[2ex]
&\qquad\qquad \left. - \log\left(1 - \frac{v^2}{c^2}\right) - \frac{v^2}{c^2}\right\} \quad \text{for } v < c/(\epsilon)^{\frac{1}{2}}, \\[3ex]
-\left(\frac{dE}{dx}\right)_b &= \frac{2\pi n e^4}{mv^2}\left\{\frac{2b\omega_0(\epsilon)^{\frac{1}{2}}}{v}K_0\left(\frac{b\omega_0(\epsilon)^{\frac{1}{2}}}{v}\right)K_1\left(\frac{b\omega_0(\epsilon)^{\frac{1}{2}}}{v}\right)\right. \\[2ex]
&\qquad\qquad \left. - \frac{1 - v^2/c^2}{\epsilon - 1} + \log\frac{\epsilon}{\epsilon - 1}\right\} \quad \text{for } v > c/(\epsilon)^{\frac{1}{2}},
\end{aligned}\right\} \quad (3)
$$

whereas the Bohr theory gives

$$
-\left(\frac{dE}{dx}\right)_b = \frac{2\pi n e^4}{mv^2}\left\{\log\left(\frac{1.123 \cdot v}{\omega_0 b}\right)^2 - \log\left(1 - \frac{v^2}{c^2}\right) - \frac{v^2}{c^2}\right\}. \quad (4)
$$

In (3) K_0 and K_1 stand for the Haenkel functions of zero and first order respectively[1]. For small arguments, hence for small b, one can replace them with their asymptotic expressions

$$
K_0(x) \approx \frac{1}{2}\log\frac{4}{3.17 \cdot x^2} ; \qquad K_1(x) \approx \frac{1}{x} ;
$$

$$
3.17 = e^{2C} \text{ where } C = \text{Eulers Constant}
$$

---

[1] See for example B. WATSON: Theory of Bessel Functions, 1922, p. 78. They are $K_\nu(z) = \pi i/2 \, e^{\nu\pi i/2} H_\nu^{(1)}(iz)$.

and thus obtain

$$-\left(\frac{dE}{dx}\right)_b = \frac{2\pi ne^4}{mv^2}\left\{\log\left(\frac{1.123v}{\omega_0 b(\epsilon)^{\frac{1}{2}}}\right)^2 - \log\left(1 - \frac{v^2}{c^2}\right) - \frac{v^2}{c^2}\right\} \text{ for } v < c/(\epsilon)^{\frac{1}{2}},$$

$$-\left(\frac{dE}{dx}\right)_b = \frac{2\pi ne^4}{mv^2}\left\{\log\left(\frac{1.123v}{\omega_0 b(\epsilon)^{\frac{1}{2}}}\right)^2 - \frac{1 - v^2/c^2}{\epsilon - 1} + \log\frac{\epsilon}{\epsilon - 1}\right\} \text{ for } v > c/(\epsilon)^{\frac{1}{2}}. \tag{5}$$

For $\epsilon = 1$ the first of these two expressions goes over into the Bohr expression (4). The calculation of the energy loss with the help of the radiation vector S is, thus, in its end result equivalent to the Bohr calculation which sums the energy transferred to the individual electrons through collisions. The Fermi calculation thus teaches a new conception of the nature of this energy loss. But, contrary to the expressions (4) and (5), which are valid only for small values of b, (3) holds quite generally. For large values of b, the first term in this equation vanishes exponentially, while the other two terms remain constant. This term thus gives an energy flux which goes out from an arbitrarily large cylinder, and thus represents an energy radiation. This is nothing more than the electromagnetic radiation, already observed by Cerenkov (C 2), when fast electrons pass through matter. The energy contained in these terms is thus given off in the collision process, not as kinetic energy of knock-on electrons, but in the form of radiation.

Whereas the difference between the result of Fermi and of Bohr for $v < c/(\epsilon)^{\frac{1}{2}}$ is of small consequence and lies only in the factor ϵ in the logarithm, there is a difference in character for $v > c/(\epsilon)^{\frac{1}{2}}$: the term $-\log(1 - v^2/c^2)$, which tends towards infinity as $v \to c$ and results in the logarithmic increase in the energy loss according to Bohr, is not present in the Fermi theory, but in its place are terms which have finite limits as $v \to c$. This fact can be understood intuitively: the logarithmic increase of the energy loss in the Bohr theory derives from the Lorenz contraction of the field of the moving particle, the contraction having the effect that the high speed particle can act in a collision-like manner on bound electrons at great distances and thus give up energy. The maximum effective collision distance thus becomes greater with increasing velocity and tends to infinity as $v \to c$. When the polarization of the medium is taken into account, the field representation in Fourier resolution is completely changed for all frequencies with propagation velocity less than the particle velocity, hence in the case $v > c/(\epsilon)^{\frac{1}{2}}$, for all frequencies less than the resonance frequency. For these frequencies there is formed a bow wave with angle different for each frequency, thus showing a dispersion, but approaching a fixed form as $v \to c$ and showing no further contraction. Hence, the maximum effective collision distance no longer approaches infinity, but rather, a fixed limiting value.

The difference between formula (5) and the Bohr formula (4), as mentioned above, also represents the corrections to be added to the complete collision formula (1). Thus we now obtain for the energy loss of a high speed charged particle the improved expression

$$-\left(\frac{dE}{dx}\right) = \frac{2\pi ne^4}{mv^2}\left\{\log\frac{mv^2W}{I^2Z^2} - \log(1 - v^2/c^2) + (1 - v^2/c^2) - \log\epsilon\right\}$$

$$\text{for } v < c/(\epsilon)^{\frac{1}{2}},$$

$$-\left(\frac{dE}{dx}\right) = \frac{2\pi ne^4}{mv^2}\left\{\log\frac{mv^2W}{I^2Z^2} + 1 - \log(\epsilon - 1) - \frac{1 - v^2/c^2}{\epsilon - 1}\right\}$$

$$\text{for } v > c/(\epsilon)^{\frac{1}{2}}.$$

$$(6)$$

For $v = c/(\epsilon)^{\frac{1}{2}}$ the two expressions merge. In the limiting case of very high energies the last term of the second expression falls completely away, and furthermore, the quantity IZ can be replaced by the corresponding expression $\hbar\omega_0$ of our model and $\epsilon - 1$ by $4\pi ne^2/m\omega_0^2$. One then obtains the formula for loss of energy by collisions valid in the limit of very high energies,

$$-\left(\frac{dE}{dx}\right) = \frac{2\pi ne^4}{mc^2}\left\{\log\frac{\pi m^2c^2W}{ne^2h^2} + 1\right\}. \tag{7}$$

According to this formula, the energy loss at very high energies depends no longer upon the nature of the absorbing medium but only on the electron density prevailing therein; this is of such a nature that the energy loss becomes less with increasing density.

The energy loss at low energies depends on the value of ϵ. This quantity in the simplified Fermi model is the static dielectric constant. In considering real matter this must be replaced by an effective value which is given in an originally unknown manner by the dispersion characteristics of the material. In this respect there is some uncertainty in the application of the collision formulae (6). In order to evaluate the influence of this uncertainty, Fermi calculated the energy loss of ordinary electrons in water, at one time assigning the value $\epsilon = 1.7$ and at another time the value $\epsilon = 1.1$. The results are compiled in table I. It is seen that the difference with respect to the old theory ($\epsilon = 1$) becomes appreciable only for energies at which the energy loss is preponderantly determined by the radiation losses; hence the preceding formulae lose their significance.

Table 1.

Electron energy		10^6	10^7	10^8 eV
Energy loss	$\epsilon = 1$	1.93	2.15	2.72 MeV/cm
	$\epsilon = 1.1$	1.92	1.91	2.09 ''
	$\epsilon = 1.7$	1.83	1.75	1.94 ''

In the case of heavy particles, protons, deuterons, and α-particles, the radiation losses set in only at much higher energies. On the other hand, the velocities of these particles, up to energies of a few MeV, still lie so far below the velocity of light that the first of the two formulae (6) is applicable, and it differs from the old collision-loss formula by only a few percent. Thus, measurable effects do not occur here either.

It is different in the case of the mesons. Here such high energies are available that, on the one hand, the differences between the old and the new collision-loss formulae must be quite noticeable without, on the other hand, the radiation losses playing any essential rôle. Fig. 1 shows the energy losses calculated according to (1) and (6), respectively, in air, water, and lead. One sees that, according to formula (1), the energy loss in the various substances at low energies shows a systematic variation with the atomic

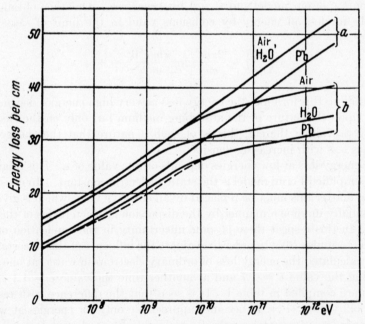

Figure 1. Energy loss of mesons in air, water, and lead in units $2\pi n e^4/m v^2$, a) according to Bohr-Bloch, b) according to Fermi.

number of the absorbing substance, whereas at the higher energies, according to the new theory, there is a systematic dependence on the density. The point where the transition takes place, as well as the more exact course of the curve in this vicinity, depends upon the assumed value of ϵ. The dash curve, which refers to lead, indicates the results of Wick's calculation (W 6), which has drawn upon empirical data from optics for the calculation of the course of the curve in the transition region. In a precise calculation of this nature the transition is somewhat smoothed over, but the difference with respect to the Fermi calculation is practically without significance. At any rate, one sees that with meson energies of 10^{10} volts, in spite of nearly identical atomic numbers, there is already a noticeably weaker absorption in water than in a layer of air of the same number of electrons.

In order to clarify the question of the extent to which this effect can explain the difference found experimentally between the absorption in water and in air, Fermi has discussed Ehmert's measurements (E 1), as well as those by Rossi, Hilberry and Hoag (R 9), on the basis of his collision-loss formula, which he applied in the form (7), valid for high energies. Ehmert finds that the number of mesons behind thick layers of air (> 10 m. water equivalent) amounts to only about half of that behind a corresponding layer of water, and that the remaining rays fall off with the 1.87 power of the depth measured in meters of water. The latter fact can be explained, according to Euler and Heisenberg (E 7), if it is assumed that the number of mesons of energy greater than E at the point of their creation is given by a power law of the form $N = c \cdot E^{-1.87}$, and that these mesons are then absorbed with a constant energy loss.—According to (7), the energy loss for mesons of 10^{10} eV is 2.2 MeV/g cm.$^{-2}$ in water and is 2.8 MeV/g cm.$^{-2}$ in air of the mean density of the atmosphere (= 1/e of the density at the earth's surface). The limiting energies of mesons which are just able to pass through a thick water layer and a thick air layer, respectively, are in the ratio of 2.2:2.8, and the numbers of surviving mesons are in the ratio $(2.8:2.2)^{1.87} = 1.58$. Ehmert's measurements give for this ratio the value 2. Since the theoretical evaluation resulting from the application of equation (7) doubtless gives an upper limit of the value to be expected on the basis of the Fermi effect, it must be concluded that this effect can explain, at the most, 50% of the observed effect. The remaining difference must be ascribed as before to a decay of the meson.

This comes out even more significantly in considering the experiments by Rossi, Hilberry, and Hoag, who have measured the variation of the meson intensity in the atmosphere and at various depths have determined the decrease due to the insertion of a graphite layer of 82 g/cm.^{2} in the radiation path. This decrease is again only half of that of an equivalent layer of air. Since in such a thin absorber only the slowest mesons (up to 10^{8} eV) are taken out, the Fermi effect is of almost no importance; an evaluation shows that it can not account for even 10% of the measured difference. Hence, these experiments lend weight to the decay theory of the mesons and give a decay period of $2 \cdot 10^{-6}$ sec.

A more precise discussion of meson absorption has been undertaken by Lyons (L 12). He took into account the energy dependence of the collision losses, together with the spectral distribution of the mesons, for which he assumed a power law of the form $N = a \cdot E^{-\gamma}$ (N = number of mesons at the place of their creation with energy greater than E). If decay is left out of consideration, as is allowable in solid or liquid substances, the Fermi collision-loss formula shows that the total number of mesons behind an absorbing layer is to be calculated by ascribing to a meson of energy E a range R on the basis of the relation

$$R = 0.5 \cdot E^{0.96}, \ E \text{ in } 10^8 \text{eV}, \ R \text{ in } m \ H_2O.$$

Here it is to be remarked that from this relation, which is calculated with the help of the *mean* energy, one cannot draw immediate conclusions on the *most probable* energy loss of a single meson such as appears in Wilson chamber measurements. The distribution of energy loss for a single particle is given by an asymmetrical probability curve whose maximum lies at a lower energy value than its mean value. According to Lyons the mean energy loss in 1 m. H_2O for a meson of 10^{11}eV energy is about $3 \cdot 10^8$eV, whereas the most probable energy loss is only about $2.2 \cdot 10^8$eV.—The above energy range relation holds for $\gamma \lesssim 2$. With the help of the depth relation measured by Ehmert, $N = c \cdot T^{-1.87}$ one can thus undertake a more precise determination of γ, with the result that $\gamma = 1.87 \cdot 0.96 = 1.80$.

At very great depths of water, according to Wilson's measurements, the Ehmert exponent 1.87 for the dependence on depth increases to a value of about 2.5. According to Lyons, this phenomenon can be explained by an additional energy loss, which sets in only for very high meson energies ($\gtrsim 10^{11}$eV) and is in practically quantitative agreement with the cross section for excitation of Hoffman bursts at great depths as measured by Schein and Gill (S 3). Whether this energy loss has to do with an absorption term for mesons of spin 1 coming in at high energies according to a calculation by Oppenheimer, Snyder, and Serber (O 2), or whether it is simply a radiation loss must, however, remain unanswered.

The discussion of meson absorption in the atmosphere and in shallow depths of water also leads, according to the more precise calculation of Lyons, to the result that one has to assume a decay of the meson. The best agreement with the experimental results is obtained if one ascribes to the meson a mean life of $3 \cdot 10^{-6}$ sec.

7. BURST EXCITATION BY MESONS

By C. F. v. WEIZSÄCKER, Strasbourg

1. Identification of Bursts with the Penetrating Component

The "bursts" in the ionization chamber discovered by Hoffmann consist preponderantly of a very large number of electrons of both signs appearing simultaneously and thus constitute simply the very largest "showers." Part of the bursts undoubtedly have their origin in the soft component; these bursts evidently occur when a portion of a large air shower strikes the chamber walls. Other bursts, however, must be ascribed to the hard component. This analysis has been thoroughly studied by Euler and Heisenberg (E 7). Consequently we will follow their discussion of Nie's burst production curve (N 3).

Fig. 1 shows the dependence of the number of those bursts, which contain more than 200 particles, upon the thickness of the absorbing layer placed above the chamber. The maximum of the curve is to be ascribed to the soft component, since its height and its dependence on the thickness and material of the layer correspond to the predictions of the cascade theory. The maximum in lead is the greatest and occurs for very thin layers,

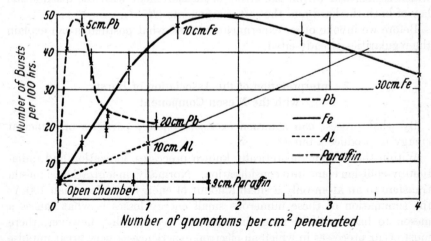

Figure 1. Burst yield curve for Pb, Fe, Al and parafin. Only bursts > 4 MeV (according to NIE).

(calculated in $g/cm.^2$); in iron it is smaller and occurs at a greater thickness, and in aluminum it cannot be seen at all.

On the other hand, at very great thicknesses, the number of bursts which is nearly independent of the thickness of the layer, cannot derive from the soft component but only from a radiation which has a very small absorption coefficient. We, therefore, ascribe them to the mesons as a secondary effect. Yet in every respect they behave as normal cascades which have built up in the absorbing layer. They differ from the cascades at the maximum of the curve only in the fact that the primary electron or light quantum which released the cascade did not come into the absorbing layer from above but was excited or accelerated within the layer by a meson.

What conclusions can be drawn from the experiments on the primary process of creation of the first particle of the cascade? Apparently its dependence upon the nuclear charge differs from that of the cascade excitation itself. According to Fig. 1 it is weakest in lead and strongest in aluminum; admitting the uncertainty which lies in the fact that the curves have been measured up to actual saturation only in the case of lead, it seems to be true that the probability of the process does not increase with Z.

The dependence of the number of bursts on their size is also important. This throws some light on the energy distribution law of the particles which excite the burst. The experiments (Sittkus (S 18), Schein and Gill (S 3)) show that the number $N(S)$ of bursts, in which more than S particles are present, varies as $S^{-\gamma}$, in which the exponent γ lies in the neighborhood of 2. Since, on the average, the energy consumed in a burst is proportional to the number of particles, S, the bursts show a distribution law which is identical within the errors of measurement with the distribution law of both the hard and the soft components ($E^{-1\cdot8}$).

Before we invoke other experiments we ask what postulates can explain the regularities already cited.

2. Interpretation of the Association of Bursts with the Meson Component

By what process can a meson excite secondary particles of sufficient energy to produce a burst?

Within the field of theoretically known processes, ionization and radiation-by-collision come into consideration. Normally, in ionization, a meson transfers to an atom only a small amount of energy, i.e., less than 100eV; the summation of these numerous small energy losses is what causes a meson to have a finite range in matter. Occasionally, however, there must occur processes in which an electron experiences a very great impulse and extracts a considerable fraction of the energy from the meson. Likewise, through radiation-by-collision, a correspondingly large fraction of the energy can be transferred to a light quantum, which can then start a cascade. It is true that mesons were first differentiated from electrons by the fact that they excite no radiation-by-collision. However, collision-radiation processes must occur on very long paths, at least as frequently as in the ratio of the squares of the masses of the electron and the meson.

Another possibility is to assume a Heisenberg "Explosion" as the origin of the bursts, i.e., the excitation of many particles in a single elementary act. As Heisenberg (cf. Chapt. 12, Heisenberg) has remarked, there is really no significant difference between this and the previous interpretation, for the explosions will take place only when a great deal of energy is transferred by an interaction of the meson with matter. It would, therefore, seem reasonable to investigate this interaction along the lines of the normal theory and in this manner first to ask whether what one calculates is the probability for the excitation of a single secondary particle, as is usually assumed in the statement of the standard theory, or whether in the process many particles are automatically created as "by products" (cf. the investigations of Bloch and Nordsieck on the emission of light in the Rutherford scattering, and the work of Heisenberg on meson showers; Chapt. 12, Heisenberg).

Bhabha (B 19) has calculated the effective cross-section for the excitation of a very fast electron by a meson (the "knock-on" process). The energy dependence of his formula, however, is not in agreement with the experimental results. If we designate by ϵ that fraction of the energy of the meson which is transferred to the electron (ϵ is, therefore, a pure number: $0 \leq \epsilon < 1$), then, according to Bhabha, the effective cross-section is proportional to $d\epsilon/\epsilon^2$. This means that on a percentage basis very small energy transfers are favored. If one takes a spectrum of the mesons in which the number $N_m(E)$ of those mesons with energy greater than E is proportional to $E^{-\gamma}$ then, on account of the prevalence of small energy transfers, the number $N_e(E)$ of knock-on electrons with energy greater than E is proportional to $E^{-\gamma-1}$, whereas the experiments require that this quantity be proportional to $E^{-\gamma}$.

One can conclude from this that the primary process of energy transfer must, in the final analysis, have a cross-section which is more nearly proportional to $d\epsilon/\epsilon$. Then, although the small energy transfers are more probable than the large ones, the mean energy transferred in a collision is proportional to $\int \epsilon \frac{d\epsilon}{\epsilon}$; as an example, if it extends from $\epsilon = 0$ to $\epsilon = 1/4$, the integral has the same value as from $\epsilon = 1/4$ to $\epsilon = 1/2$; that is, the energy transferred in an ϵ-interval is independent of ϵ, and hence the primary spectrum is exactly reproduced in the bursts.

The dependence of the process on the material will be discussed in section 5.

3. Application to Radiation at Great Depths

Although the burst excitation is quite rare, it must contribute to a certain extent to the absorption of mesons. This contribution should make itself noticeable at very great depths.

In the first approximation the intensity of the cosmic radiation at great depths (from sea level to a depth of about 1000 m. water equivalent) can be again represented by the power law, with which we are already familiar. If T is the depth from the top of the atmosphere measured in $gm/cm.^2$ or in cm. water equivalent, then the intensity of the radiation at great depths is nearly proportional to $T^{-\gamma}$ where γ again has about the value 1.9 (Clay (C 4), Wilson (W 13), Ehmert (E 2)). This is immediately understandable theoretically, if the mesons are stopped exclusively by ionization processes, because then each meson has a fixed range proportional to its energy. If a is the energy loss of a meson per cm. H_2O, then at the depth T all mesons with energy greater than Ta are still present. Thus the energy spectrum is transformed immediately into the absorption curve (cf. Euler and Heisenberg).

Experimentally, however, the absorption law is not exactly $T^{-\gamma}$. The absorption takes place considerably more slowly than this law requires over the first 100 m. H_2O and somewhat faster from 500 m. of water on down to great depths.

The initial slower absorption is a transition effect from air to water, connected with the decay of the meson (Euler and Heisenberg (E 7), Lyons (L 12)). In the atmosphere the decay plays a comparable role with the absorption by ionization, but this is not so in water or solid ground; only in the air, because of its low density, are the individual ionization processes distributed over such a long path that the meson has time to decay. Because of the dilatation of time the slow mesons decay preferentially. Therefore, in the atmosphere the number of mesons with low energy is less than corresponds to the $E^{-\gamma}$ spectrum. These slow mesons, moreover, are the first to be stopped after entry into water or earth. Therefore, fewer mesons are absorbed at first in water than would be expected from the spectrum $E^{-\gamma}$. The normal law $T^{-\gamma}$ can hold true only after the absorption of all mesons, the frequency of which was appreciably altered by decay. The effect has nothing to do with the burst process and will not be considered further at this point.

On the contrary, the increased rate of fall of the absorption curve at very great depths can be ascribed to the excitation of bursts (cf. Lyons (L 12)). We might ask what absorption law would be expected for these. By this process a meson is absorbed effectually in a single act. It does not disappear entirely but diminishes its energy by about a factor of 1/2. In this way, however, it goes over into an energy range in which, according to the $E^{-\gamma}$ law, there are many more mesons than in the original range. That is, the gap which the burst process leaves in the mesons of high energy is much more noticeable than the associated increase in the number of slow mesons, which is equal in absolute number but smaller in percentage. In a first approximation one can figure that every meson which undergoes a burst process disappears. When this fate will overtake the individual meson is a matter of chance; whereas the normal ionization reduces the meson energy slowly and gradually, the burst processes have the effect of thinning out the meson stream. Hence an exponential absorption must be superposed upon that which varies with $T^{-\gamma}$. Thus the meson intensity should vary with depth as

$$F(T) = \text{const } T^{-\gamma} e^{-\alpha T}. \tag{1}$$

The experimental results can be represented by

$$\alpha \approx \frac{1}{2000 m H_2 O}. \tag{2}$$

A proof of this theory is also afforded by the intensity of the soft radiation at great depths. Electrons which are present at a considerable depth below sea level can not stem from the primary soft component. They must have been excited by mesons. Since the decay plays no rôle, they must arise from the burst process. At least, one can regard the bursts as the most important of the production processes. It must, therefore, be possible to compute the intensity of the soft component behind great thicknesses of water from the additional exponential absorption of the mesons. According to Williams one can make the following rough calculation:

From the meson component, which can be represented as a current of energy J per cm.^{2} per sec., the exponential absorption extracts the energy $J \alpha dT$ in the element of path dT. This energy is transferred to the soft component. Since the process is stationary in time, the soft component must lose the same energy in the same distance. Through ionization an electron loses about the same energy a per cm. H_2O as a meson. Hence, in the distance dT the soft component loses the energy $a \, dT$ per particle; since its total loss in this distance is the energy $J \alpha dT$, it must contain $\dfrac{J\alpha}{a}$

particles per cm.^{2} per sec. For comparison, we must know the number of particles in the meson component. Since we have assumed the total energy J of all mesons as a known quantity, we need to know the mean energy of a meson. The number of mesons of energy greater than E at depth T is proportional to $(E + aT)^{-\gamma}$ since the mesons which have energy E at depth T had originally the energy $E + aT$. Here the additional absorption has been overlooked, and the calculation is valid only for depths which are small compared with 2000 meters of H_2O. The number of mesons with energy between E and $E + dE$ is consequently proportional to $(E + aT)^{-\gamma-1}dE$, and the mean energy

$$\bar{E} = \frac{\int_0^\infty (E + aT)^{-\gamma-1}E\,dE}{\int_0^\infty (E + aT)^{-\gamma-1}dE} = \frac{aT}{\gamma - 1} \approx 1.25aT. \qquad (3)$$

The mean energy of the mesons, therefore, increases in proportion to the depth. This becomes evident when one recalls that the primary spectrum $E^{-\gamma}$ diverges at $E = 0$; thus, if it is not modified for small values of E, it gives a zero mean energy. However, the absorption soon disposes of the excess of slow mesons. The number of mesons is, therefore, $J(\gamma - 1)/aT$, and the ratio of the number of electrons to the mesons is $N_e/N_m = \alpha T/(\gamma - 1.)$. The relative intensity of the soft component must, therefore, increase with the depth T. This follows immediately from the increase of the mean meson energy with the depth, since the more energetic a meson is, the more electrons it can excite in a burst.

In a depth of 400 meters H_2O a ratio $N_e/N_m \approx 0.25$ is to be expected. The experimental results give

Author	T in m. H_2O	N_e/N_m
Auger-Grivet .	30	0.07
Clay	300	0.11
"	427	0.22

For the quantitative comparison one is referred to the work of Lyons.

4. Theory of the Elementary Processes of Burst Excitation

Just what is the elementary process which we have formally designated as a "burst process"?

The calculation by Bhabha takes account only of the interaction of the electric field of the meson with the impacted electron. Oppenheimer, Snyder, and Serber (O 2) have raised the point that with the spin of the meson there is associated a magnetic moment, which for very close collisions gives rise to a very much larger interaction than the electric charge. Even more than in direct ionization this interaction shows up in a strong radiation-by-collision. Christy and Kusaka (C 3) have evaluated all of the effective cross-sections of interest. In what follows we give their results with a few explanations.

The effective cross sections are evaluated for three possible spin values of the meson: 0, $1/2\hbar$, and $1\hbar$. Although the experiments of nuclear physics show that a meson of spin 0 is not satisfactory, this value is included since recent hypotheses suggest the existence of various kinds of mesons with different spins (cf. section 5 and the 10th Chapter on the theory of mesons). The spin $1/2\hbar$ is included in the interest of completeness although the mesons responsible for the nuclear forces, according to Yukawa's hypothesis, must have whole valued spins. The values of the magnetic moment listed are those which are derived from the usual field equations without additional terms introduced *ad hoc*. At the same time they are the values for which the calculated effective cross-section has the smallest possible value. Moreover, the empirical value of the magnetic moment of the proton and of the neutron shows that an elementary particle need not necessarily have the "normal" magnetic moment. The effective cross-sections listed are, therefore, the lowest values since direct measurements of the magnetic moment of the meson are not available.

In the formulae the symbols signify the following: μ, the meson mass, m, the electron mass, $\alpha = e^2/\hbar c$ the Sommerfeld constant, Z, the charge of the nucleus at which the process takes place, E_0, the primary energy of the meson, ϵ, the fraction of the energy transferred to the electron or light quantum. $\epsilon_m \approx [1 + (\mu^2 c^2/2mE_0)]^{-1} \approx E_0/(E_0 + 10^{10}\text{eV})$ is the maximum fraction of the energy which can be transferred at once. As long as the meson travels more slowly than light, the electron can at most take on the velocity of the meson and, consequently, only a small fraction of its energy, which is proportional to E_0. If, on the other hand, the meson travels with practically the velocity of light, the value of ϵ_m approaches the value 1.

$\omega = \left(\dfrac{e^2}{mc^2}\right)^2 \alpha Z^2 \approx Z^2 \cdot 1.6 \cdot 10^{-32}$ cm^2 is the unit in which we measure the effective cross-sections.

$$\frac{\sigma(E_0,\epsilon)d\epsilon}{\omega} = \qquad (4)$$

Spin	Magn. Moment	
		I. Impact with an electron
0	0	$\dfrac{2\pi}{\alpha Z}\dfrac{\mu}{m}\dfrac{\mu c^2}{E_0}\dfrac{d\epsilon}{\epsilon^2}\left(1-\dfrac{\epsilon}{\epsilon_m}\right),$
$\dfrac{1}{2}$	$\dfrac{e\hbar}{2\mu c}$	$\dfrac{2\pi}{\alpha Z}\dfrac{\mu}{m}\dfrac{\mu c^2}{E_0}\dfrac{d\epsilon}{\epsilon^2}\left(1-\dfrac{\epsilon}{\epsilon_m}+\dfrac{\epsilon^2}{2}\right),$
1	$\dfrac{e\hbar}{2\mu c}$	$\dfrac{2\pi}{\alpha Z}\dfrac{\mu}{m}\dfrac{\mu c^2}{E_0}\dfrac{d\epsilon}{\epsilon^2}\left[1-\dfrac{\epsilon}{\epsilon_m}+\dfrac{\epsilon^2}{3}+\dfrac{mE_0\epsilon}{3\mu^2 c^2}\left(1-\dfrac{\epsilon}{\epsilon_m}+\dfrac{\epsilon^2}{2}\right)\right].$
		II. Collision-radiation
0	0	$\dfrac{16}{3}\dfrac{(1-\epsilon)}{\epsilon}d\epsilon\left[\log\dfrac{2(1-\epsilon)E_0}{(5/6)\mu c^2 Z^{1/3}\epsilon}-\dfrac{1}{2}\right],$
$\dfrac{1}{2}$	$\dfrac{e\hbar}{2\mu c}$	$\dfrac{16}{3}\left(\dfrac{3\epsilon}{4}+\dfrac{1-\epsilon}{\epsilon}\right)d\epsilon\left[\log\dfrac{2(1-\epsilon)E_0}{(5/6)\mu c^2 Z^{1/3}\epsilon}-\dfrac{1}{2}\right],$
1	$\dfrac{e\hbar}{2\mu c}$	$d\epsilon\left[\dfrac{\pi E_0}{5\mu c^2 Z^{1/3}}\left(\dfrac{2-2\epsilon+7\epsilon^2}{12}\right)+\cdots\right].$

In the last expression, which gives the collision-radiation for meson spin 1 additive terms which increase only logarithmically with E_0 have been omitted.

The calculations show that the collision-radiation must be made responsible for the large bursts; this is indicated by the fact that the electron impact processes have the factor $d\epsilon/\epsilon^2$ (only for spin 1 is there a term in $d\epsilon/\epsilon$). From the theoretical standpoint can the calculated cross-sections now be applied without further consideration?

In all three cases the calculated cross-sections must be in error for very high values of the meson energy E_0, but for different reasons. The collision-radiation originates, in the cases of spin 0 and spin $1/2\hbar$, from transitions of the meson at the nucleus, transitions in which the separation between the meson and the nucleus can be quite large. The logarithmic increase of the cross-section with E_0 follows from the fact that the greater the energy the greater the collision-distances which contribute to the effect. This increase is limited, however, to collision-distances which are less than the mean atomic radius since the nuclear field has no further effect on the meson on account of the shielding by the electron shells. This comes into play at an energy $E_0 \approx \dfrac{\mu^2 c^3}{\hbar} \cdot \dfrac{\hbar^2}{Z^{1/3} me^2} \approx 5 \cdot 10^{11}$ eV. Above this energy the effective cross-section remains constant.

On the other hand, the collision-radiation with spin 1 arises from transitions very close to the nucleus. In this case, however, the formula is in error for another reason. In its derivation it is assumed that the interaction between the meson and the nucleus is small; the Born collision theory was used in the calculation. This assumption becomes incorrect for $E_0 \approx 2 \cdot 10^{10}$ eV. It is to be assumed that above this energy single excitation of a light quantum generally does not occur, but an "explosion" takes place with the simultaneous excitation of many particles (presumably mostly mesons). Christy and Kusaka have attempted to derive a lower limit for the cross-section at very high energies. Most of the interaction arises from radiation of high frequency (above 137 $\mu c^2/\hbar$). The authors calculate only that contribution to the collision-radiation which is made by frequencies below this limit. If one makes the plausible but unproven assumption that radiation of high frequency is diminished by a non-linear interference phenomenon while that of lower frequencies is not, the cross-section so calculated should be regarded as a minimum value. This gives

$$\frac{\sigma(E_0,\epsilon)d\epsilon}{\omega} = A\left(1 + \log\frac{\pi E_0}{5A\mu c^2 Z^{1/3}}\right)\left(\frac{2 - 2\epsilon + 7\epsilon^2}{12}\right)d\epsilon + \cdots. \qquad (5)$$

Here A is a constant which to a certain degree measures the cutoff frequency in units $\mu c^2/\hbar$ and here would be set equal to 137. The terms omitted here are independent of A.

5. Comparison with Experiment. The Spin of the Meson

We now have the question whether the processes introduced above are sufficient to explain the observed bursts. This seems to be so; at the same time it gives unexpected information on the spin of the meson. The dependence of burst excitation on the material comes out, according to calculations by Oppenheimer (O 1) and by Christy and Kusaka, in essential agreement with the experiments. We will not, however, describe these calculations here in detail. The dependence of burst frequency on burst size is represented in Fig. 2. Here the curves show the theoretical relations, and the dots are the experimental values of Schein and Gill. Curve 1 corresponds to spin 1 according to equation (5), curve 2 to spin 1 according to equation (4), curves 3 and 4 to the spins 1/2 and 0 respectively. We are forced to the conclusion that the bursts are set off by mesons of spin 0 (or, at the most, of 1/2).

This result appears surprising if we recall that nuclear physics, from which the idea of mesons originated, requires a meson spin not equal to zero to represent correctly the behavior of nuclear forces. The contradiction may be relieved, and, at the same time, a whole series of new experiments is suggested, if it is assumed that there are two kinds of mesons, some of spin 1 and some of spin 0.

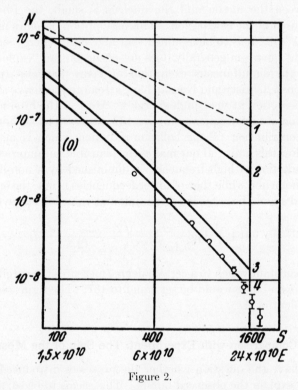

Figure 2.

This thought was first put forward in the theory of Möller and Rosenfeld (M 5) on nuclear forces. These authors showed that the divergence of the nuclear forces, at least in the classical approximation, could be eliminated by the assumption of two cooperating meson fields with field strengths transformed as a vector or as a pseudoscalar and belonging to mesons of spin 1 or zero respectively. Intuitively, one can say that the two kinds of particles give, in themselves, a divergent law of force, but that, by suitable superposition of their effects, the divergent part can be eliminated while a finite force remains. Whereas one can object to this theory on the grounds that it leaves unexplained the quantum theoretical divergence, yet it has become more plausible for reasons now to be enumerated.

One of the most important difficulties with the meson theory is the difference between the two values of the mean life of the meson, the one resulting from nuclear physics and the other from cosmic radiation. According to cosmic ray measurements the meson must live from 10 to 100 times longer than Yukawa had concluded from β-decay. This contradiction is clarified if it is assumed that both the nuclear field and the cosmic radiation contain two kinds of mesons, and that one of the mesons has a long life while the other has a short life; then one should always observe the short life in β-decay since the short-lived mesons would precede the long-lived ones in decaying. In cosmic radiation, on the other hand, the short-lived mesons would decay in the high atmosphere, and at sea level one would observe only the long-lived ones.

Nevertheless, in cosmic radiation one should notice some sign of the short-lived mesons; there are, indeed, strong indications of their presence. Thus Weisz (W 3) has remarked that the various determinations of the mean life of the mesons from cosmic radiation give a longer mean life in proportion to the length of the path in the atmosphere used in the measurements for traversal by the mesons. Weisz concluded from this that mesons have no unique mass value; yet any lack of uniqueness of the decay time, including the existence of the two values suggested here, together with an essentially unique value of the mass; should lead to the same result, since the short-lived mesons will have decayed more, the longer the observation path. Direct evidence for short-lived mesons at great heights has been found by Juilfs (J 16) from the directional distribution of the hard component.

If we assume that the meson of spin 1 is short-lived and that that of spin 0 is long-lived, then it is understandable that the burst measurements give meson spin 0. Other possible applications of the assumption of two kinds of mesons lie beyond the limits of this review.

8. RADIOACTIVE DECAY OF THE MESON

By W. HEISENBERG, Berlin-Dahlem

According to the Yukawa Theory, a stationary meson can disintegrate radioactively into an electron and a neutrino, and in the process the two particles created each receive about half of the rest mass of the meson in the form of kinetic energy. The mean life τ_0 of the stationary meson amounts to about 10^{-8} sec. according to the theory; recent work by Möller and Rosenfeld (M 5) and Rozental (R 11) have pointed out that perhaps one must distinguish between two kinds of mesons, some of spin 1 and others of spin 0, of which the former should have this short mean life, whereas the latter could have an appreciably longer life; but the latter cannot be theoretically determined without introducing new assumptions.

The fact that the mesons observed in the cosmic rays undergo radioactive disintegration was first indirectly inferred from the number of secondary electrons by Euler (E 4) (cf. also K 6a), and was later confirmed by cloud-chamber photographs by Williams and Roberts (W 12) (cf. also Kunze (K 7)). One of the most important tasks now consists of the experimental determination of the mean life τ_0. The first evaluation of this constant by Euler on the basis of the experimental results available at the time (K 6a) gave values of τ_0 between $2 \cdot 10^{-6}$ and $3 \cdot 10^{-6}$ sec. Later investigations resulted partly in larger (Pomerantz and Johnson (P 5)) and partly in smaller (Kolhörster and Matthes (K 5)) values. The most precise work of recent years has shown that the correct value of τ_0 lies somewhat below the original value of Euler, in the range

$$\tau_0 \sim 1.5 \text{ to } 2.5 \cdot 10^{-6} \text{ sec.} \tag{1}$$

These experiments will be discussed in what follows.

Up to now three fundamentally different courses have been followed to determine the decay time. First, in one way or another one can investigate the intensity of the mesons in air as a function of the path distance traversed. One then obtains the mean decay path R, a quantity which is tied in with the mean decay time τ_0 of the stationary meson, the momentum p, and the rest mass μ of the meson by the relation derived from the time dilatation of the relativity theory:

$$R = \tau_0 c \cdot \left(\frac{p}{\mu c}\right). \tag{2}$$

Secondly, one can calculate indirectly the decay time, according to the method of Euler and Williams, from the number of decay electrons in equilibrium with the meson component: thus about half of the energy $E \sim pc$ of the decaying meson is transferred on the average to the decay electron, which in turn forms a cascade. The energy $pc/2$ of the decay electron thus finally divides itself among electrons of such low energy (10^6 to 10^8eV), that these can no longer experience multiplication. Now let κ be the ratio of the number of such low energy electrons to the number of mesons. Then, in equilibrium, the energy loss of the meson per cm. because of decay must be twice as great as the energy loss per cm. of all of the electrons. The energy loss by decay is composed of two parts: the part pc/R of the moving mesons and a part associated with the mesons which have come to rest. The latter is evidently equal to the rest energy of the meson multiplied by the relative decrease per cm. of the total number of mesons by ionization, and this is given by γ/T, if dependence of intensity on depth is given by $J \sim T^{-\gamma}$. The mean energy loss a of an electron between 10^6 and 10^8eV amounts in air to about

$$a \approx 3 . 10^3 \text{eV/cm.}$$

Thus we have the relation

$$\frac{pc}{2R} + \frac{\mu c^2}{2} \frac{\gamma}{T} = \kappa a,$$

and hence

$$\kappa = \frac{\mu c^2}{2a}\left(\frac{1}{\tau_0 c} + \frac{\gamma}{T}\right). \tag{3}$$

Moreover, it will be shown later that on the basis of Rasetti's experiments (R 1) and the theoretical considerations of Tomonga and Araki (T 2) the equation (3) can hold only for the positively charged mesons.

In the third place, the decay time of the stationary meson can be measured directly if one allows the mesons to come to rest and measures the time which elapses on the average before the decay electron is emitted (Rasetti (R 1)).

The first two methods give experimental values for τ_0/μ, the latter determines τ_0. From the ratio of the results one can, in principle, infer the mass of the meson; yet it will be shown that the direct mass determination is probably more accurate than the numbers τ_0/μ and τ_0.

According to the first of the three methods mentioned, three determinations of τ_0/μ have been made in recent times. Ageno, Bernardini, Cacciapuoti, Ferretti and Wick (A 1) have found values of $\tau_0\left(\dfrac{10^8\text{eV}}{\mu c^2}\right)$ in the vicinity of 4 to 5 microseconds. In two other experiments the mean decay path was measured for mesons of various energies: Rossi and Hall (R 7) have continued an earlier experiment by Rossi, Hilberry and Hoag (R 8) and measured the absorption of the penetrating component in Denver (1616 m.) and at Echo Lake (3240 m.); Nielsen, Ryerson, Nordheim, and Morgan (N 6) have made similar comparative records in lower altitudes (125 m. and 2040 m.). The principle of the measurements is in all cases practically the same. At two different heights the absorption measurements of the penetrating component were carried out with multiple coincidences of from 4 to 6 counter tubes between which were placed lead absorbing layers. In the measurements at greater heights an amount of absorbing material was placed above the arrangement of counters which was calculated to correspond exactly to the absorption of the air layer between the two measuring stations when the decay was not taken into account. As absorbing material substances were used with atomic numbers so close to those of oxygen and nitrogen that the conversion could be made with the usual stopping formula without error.

Without the radioactive decay one should obtain the same results from the series of measurements at each height since the amount of matter traversed was the same in both cases; a small difference is to be expected because of the effect discovered by Fermi (cf. Chapt. 6, Volz) who found that the absorption in materials of different density is not exactly proportional to the total mass; the influence of the Fermi effect is small, however, and will be taken into account by a correction. The radioactive decay then has the effect that the intensity is less at the lower elevation, and the comparison of the two intensities gives directly the decay path. In this manner the intensity measurements behind various lead thicknesses serve to distinguish between meson groups in different energy ranges: those mesons which are stopped in a lead block and those which are able to pass through. For each of these meson groups one can then calculate the mean energy from the thickness of the lead and the well-known meson spectrum. The measurements then yield the mean decay path for each group. The following table gives the comparison between the average energy and the average measured decay path; they should be approximately proportional to one another.

Table 1.

	Rossi and Hall		Nielsen, Ryerson et al.			
pc (in 10^8 eV) .	5.1	13	3.50	4.55	5.6	14
R (in km) . .	4.5	13.3	2.0	2.3	2.5	8

The table shows that in each series of measurements the proportionality of R with pc is satisfactory, and, therefore, the time dilatation of the relativity theory is indirectly confirmed; the two series of measurements, however, are in poor agreement with each other.

Correspondingly, the values of τ_0/μ resulting from the two series of measurements (with different corrections) are quite different; thus Rossi and Hall find

$$\tau_0\left(\frac{10^8 eV}{\mu c^2}\right) = (3.0 \pm 0.4) \cdot 10^{-6} sec,$$

and Nielsen, Ryerson, Nordheim and Morgan find   (4)

$$\tau_0\left(\frac{10^8 eV}{\mu c^2}\right) = (1.25 \pm 0.3) \cdot 10^{-6} sec.$$

A direct determination of τ_0 has been made by Rasetti (R 1) with the arrangement shown in Fig. 1. In the figure parallel connected counters are joined by a line and designated by a letter. The coincidence recorder 1 registers the fivefold coincidences of counter tubes A-B-C-D-E, while the recorder 2 registers anti-coincidences of recorder 1 and the counter tubes F, G. Thus in 2 are registered the events in which a meson penetrates the counters A, B, C, D, enters and remains in the absorbing block (of Al or Fe), and a decay electron is sent out into one of the counters E or a meson is deflected by the absorber into a counter E. The recorders 1 and 2 have relatively low time-resolving powers ($15 \cdot 10^{-6}$ sec.). At the same time twofold coincidences $D\text{-}E$ are separated out with higher resolution by two other coincidence circuits 4 and 6, are tied in with the circuit 2 by the coincidence circuits 3 and 5, and are recorded on the registers 3 and 4. The resolving power of circuit 4, recorded on register 3, is $1.95 \cdot 10^{-6}$ sec, while that of circuit 6, recorded on register 4, is $0.76 \cdot 10^{-6}$ sec, or in another run $0.95 \cdot 10^{-6}$ sec. Designating by n_1 to n_4 the coincidences counted in a given long interval of time by counters 1 to 4, respectively, then $n_2 - n_4$ and $n_2 - n_3$ indicate, respectively, the numbers of delayed coincidences in which more than $1.95 \cdot 10^{-6}$ sec. and more than $0.76 \cdot 10^{-6}$ sec. elapsed between the response of counter D and that of one of the counters E. These differences should then be related to the mean life τ_0 of the meson by the equation

$$\frac{n_2 - n_3}{n_2 - n_4} = e^{-\frac{(1.95-0.76)\,\cdot\,10^{-6}}{\tau_0}}.$$ (5)

Rasetti found from prolonged registrations which were carried out, partly with iron and partly with aluminum as the absorber, that the mean value of τ_0 computed from (5) is

$$\tau_0 = (1.5 \pm 0.3) \cdot 10^{-6} \text{ sec.}$$

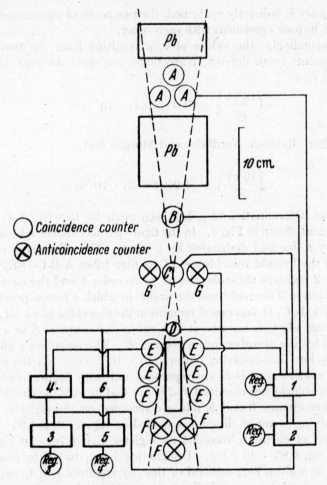

Figure 1. Rasetti's arrangement for measuring the decay time of the meson.

This value is in better agreement with the value of τ_0/μ found by Nielsen, Ryerson, Nordheim, and Morgan than with that of Rossi and Hall; thus the mass of the meson may deviate from the value $\mu c^2 = 10^8$eV by 30% at the most. The statistical error, however, is still considerable in Rasetti's measurements. For the present, therefore, it can be stated only that the value of τ_0 is smaller than was previously assumed and probably lies between 1 and 2.5 microseconds.

These small values of τ_0 and of τ_0/μ are in turn difficult to reconcile with the values deduced by Euler from the number of secondary electrons according to equation (3), especially since Bernardini, Cacciapuoti, Ferretti, Piccioni, and Wick (B 9) have shown that the number of decay electrons is even smaller than Euler had previously assumed. With the apparatus described above Rasetti has investigated in how many cases the radioactive decay of a meson stopped in the absorbing block can actually be observed. After taking account of the absorption in the block and of the solid angle filled by counter tubes E, he has found that, on the average, only about half of all mesons decay radioactively while the other half are absorbed without decay.

This result can be satisfactorily interpreted by theoretical considerations made by Tomonaga and Araki (T 2). These investigators have computed the probability for the capture of a meson in an atomic nucleus (by transfer of its energy to a nuclear particle) on the Yukawa theory. In this they find an essential difference between negative and positive mesons. The effective cross-section for capture of a negative meson satisfies the $1/v$ law for small velocities and results in a mean capture life τ_c of negative mesons which depends on the density of the material concerned; even in air, this is considerably less than the mean life for decay. (The theoretical values are of the order of $\tau_c \sim 0.3 \cdot 10^{-7}$ sec.). Slow positive mesons, on the other hand, are practically immune to capture because of the Coulomb repulsion from the atomic nuclei; hence for the positive mesons decay is very much more probable than capture.

From these considerations and Rasetti's experimental findings, one can conclude that only positive mesons decay radioactively, and that the negatives are preferentially captured by atomic nuclei and there, as a rule, produce nuclear transformations. Thus formula (3) refers only to positive mesons, and in it χ refers to the equilibrium ratio of decay electrons to the positive mesons. At sea level the number of decay electrons amounts to about 18% of the mesons, according to Bopp's discussion in Chapter 9. Since somewhat more than half of all mesons at sea level carry a positive charge, the quantity κ evaluated from the intensity of the soft component is about 0.3. From this it follows from equation (3) that:

$$\tau_0 \left(\frac{10^8 \mathrm{eV}}{\mu c^2} \right) \sim 2 \cdot 10^{-6} \mathrm{sec}.$$

This number lies in the middle between the measurements by Rossi and Hall and those by Nielsen, Ryerson, Nordheim, and Morgan, and by Rasetti.

As regards the concept of radioactive decay of the meson outlined above there is still lacking one essential point of experimental confirmation. If the negative mesons are, as a rule, captured by atomic nuclei, then they must excite a form of nuclear transformation in which the entire rest energy of the meson (about 100 MeV) can be made available for heating the nucleus and evaporating nuclear particles.   One should, therefore, regularly see at the end of a track of a negative meson in a cloud chamber, a nuclear transformation with frequent emission of several protons.   Thus far no observations of this kind have been reported.

9. THE DECAY ELECTRONS OF MESONS

By Fritz Bopp, Breslau (temporarily at Berlin-Dahlem)

The soft component E (electron component) of the cosmic radiation contains at sea level, in addition to a slight residual R of cascades (see Chapter 1, Heisenberg), a secondary radiation derived from the penetrating component M (meson component) and made up of several parts of different progeny. The mesons can produce secondary cascades, first, by knock-on interaction with the irradiated matter and second, by β-decay. (Euler and Heisenberg (E 7)) (knock-on component W, decay component Z). In what follows there will be described some recent attempts which seek to determine the Z-component.

Fundamentally, any measurement is adaptable to this purpose if it displays the instability of the meson, because, as was shown by Euler and Heisenberg (E 7), there is a close connection between the intensity of the decay component in relation to that of the mesons and the mean life τ_0 of the stationary meson. Wick (B 8) and his collaborators have derived this relation, independently of the restricted assumptions of the cascade theory, on the basis of the postulate invoked by Williams, (W 10) namely, that finally the total energy transferred to the decay electrons—in the mean, therefore, half of the meson energy—must be transformed into work of ionization. If one introduces the fact discovered by Rasetti, (R 1) that only half of all mesons decay (cf. Chapter 8, Heisenberg), this equation becomes

$$\frac{Z}{M} = \frac{\mu c^2}{4a}\left(\frac{1}{c\tau} + \frac{\gamma}{T}\right). \tag{1}$$

Here μc^2 is the rest energy of the meson, a is the energy lost by ionization per cm. of path in air, and T is the depth below the top of the atmosphere in cm. air equivalent (referred to the density of air at the place of observations, thus $T = 7.5 \cdot 10^5$ cms.).

The first term gives the portion from the moving mesons, and the second term is from the mesons decaying at rest after they have been stopped. The value of a, at the ionization limit $E_i = 0.15 \cdot 10^9$eV, appears to be a useful mean value for the ionization loss, since the energies of most particles in a shower lie in the vicinity of E_i. According to Bethe (B 11 and B 26), for this case $a = 3000$ eV/cm. in air at normal pressure. In equation (1) no account is taken of the fact that decay electrons at the place of observation arise from mesons which have decayed on the average a few radiation units higher up. This must increase the ratio Z/M. On the other hand, only particles which are above a certain energy are detected by a coincidence arrangement, a consideration which diminishes the number of effective particles. Wick and his collaborators (B 8) believe that the latter effect predominates so that equation (1) should give too large rather than too small values.

According to recent measurements of the anomalous absorption of the hard component by Nielsen, Ryerson, Nordheim, and Morgan (N 5) (cf. Chapt. 8 Heisenberg), the very low value, $\tau\left(\dfrac{10^8 \mathrm{e\,V}}{\mu c^2}\right) = 1.25$ microseconds, was given for the mean life of the meson, so that according to equation (1), with $\mu c^2 = 80$ MeV, one would expect for the decay component $Z/M = 24\%$. Other measurements give, in the main, higher values for the mean life, up to 4.5 microseconds, and lead to values of Z/M all the way down to about 5%. The higher values agree qualitatively with those to be expected from the analysis of the soft component at sea level. The measurements by various authors (for example Auger, Leprince-Ringuet, and Ehrenfest (A 8)) give approximately $E/M = 30\%$. According to Euler (E 3 and E 4), the portion of decay electrons should be of this same order of magnitude, since, according to the cascade theory, there should be practically no primary electrons at sea level, and since the knock-on electron component W may be regarded as small (Auger and Rosenberg (A 12), Bernardini, Cacciapuoti and Ferretti (B 8), Grivet-Meyer (G 9), Wilson (W 14), Santangelo and Scrocco (S 1)).

Siegert (S 17) has attempted to determine the intensity of the latter independently of the decay component. Behind layers of matter of sufficient thickness the Z-component is reduced by absorption to a small residual arising from the decay of stationary mesons, so that practically the only remaining electrons are the knock-on electrons produced in the absorber. Their intensity agrees satisfactorily with that of the knock-on electrons in air if the atomic numbers of the absorber and of air are taken into account. Siegert's measurements give for the soft component under the open sky $E/M = 31.6\%$, and behind a layer of water 3 radiation units thick he gives $E/M = 20.5\%$. The first value agrees with those of other authors (Nielsen and Morgan (N 4), Stuhlinger (S 23), Street, Woodward, and Stevenson (S 22), Auger (A 7)) within the limits of error. The second value is not in agreement with other measurements if it is assumed that the water layer used was thick enough to absorb all of the decay electrons; behind a layer of stone four times as thick Wick (B 9) and his collaborators obtained only a 5% knock-on component instead of the 20% cited above. It was also reported by the same authors that Santangelo and Scrocco obtained the same value behind twice again as great a thickness.   Measurements by Pomerantz (P 4) are also in agreement with this value.   Only Alexeeva's measurements (A 2) made with absorbers 4 to 5 radiation units thick check with those by Siegert.

From examination of the various data it must be concluded that a considerable fraction of the decay electrons can penetrate through shields from 3 to 5 radiation units thick.   In fact, one might expect only a small degree of absorption in shields that are not too thick since the spectrum of the decay electrons falls off only inversely with the first power of the energy. A calculation on the basis of the cascade theory (Bopp (B 30)) gives about a 40% penetration through a water layer 3 radiation units thick.   The fractions obtained for the decay and for the knock-on electrons—as usual neglecting the residual primary electrons—are

$$Z/M = 18.5\%, \qquad W/M = 13.1\%, \tag{2}$$

values which appear to agree rather well with the above measurements. Moreover, Alexeeva's measurements (A 2) fit in with these considerations. However, his conclusion regarding the relatively strong absorption of very thin layers hardly applies to the medium thicknesses exclusively used by him.   According to the cascade theory a relatively rapid decrease of intensity or, under certain circumstances, a similar rise of intensity, can take place until an equilibrium characteristic of the material between particles and quanta is reached.

In the above analysis of the soft component the assumption is made that the intensity of the primary cascades is practically zero.   This is based upon the following considerations: In the first place the theoretically calculated latitude effect of the primary cascades at sea level amounts to only 1/10 of the observed latitude effect of the hard component.   Empirically, however, the latitude effect of the soft component agrees approximately with that of the hard component.   In the second place measurements by Bowen, Millikan and Neher (B 32) show that the cascades of electrons in a narrow band of primary energies have in the upper atmosphere an intensity variation which agrees almost exactly with that derived theoretically.   The excess of intensity at sea level must, therefore, be of secondary origin.   In the third place, according to Euler (E 5) one can evaluate the intensity of the R-component (residual primary electrons) from the frequency of large bursts since extensive showers and the large Hoffman bursts arise from the residue of very energetic primary electrons. This turns out to be negligible.

Bernardini, Cacciapuoti, Ferretti, Piccioni, and Wick (B 9) have attempted in the above mentioned work to confirm this indirect conclusion by direct measurement.   They determine the intensity of the soft component at sea level under the open sky and on a mountain behind an absorber which compensates for the thickness of air between the two stations. The excess of intensity at sea level should be equal to the intensity of the decay electrons created between the two stations and, in general, equal to the intensity of the Z-component if the thickness of the absorber is enough to prevent any of the decay electrons produced above from passing through. The authors discuss the results of their measurements on the basis of the latter assumption, which, according to the above analysis of the various determinations of the W-component, may not be quite right. In the following analysis the results of calculations on the absorption of decay electrons (Bopp (B 30)) will be used.

Table 1.

E/M in %	A	B	C
Valley Station . .	25.0	22.5	33.3
Mountain Station	26.2	31.1	51.6

The results of investigations by Wick and his collaborators are shown in column A of the above table and may be compared with the measurements by the Duke University group (Nielsen, Ryerson, Nordheim and Morgan (N 5 and 6)) taken under exactly similar conditions and shown in columns B and C (cf. Fig. 1). The latter measurements were carried out for another purpose (cf. Chapt. 8, Heisenberg) but they provide a measurement of the fraction of the intensity due to the soft component and are, therefore, useful for determining the intensity of the decay component. At least they are useful as a critique of the first work. The important data regarding the conditions of the two experiments are shown in the following synopsis.

Table 2.

Measurement	A	B	C
Valley station	Rome 50 m	Durham	123.5 m above sea
Mountain station	Cervinia 2050 m	Mt. Mitchell	2040 m
Coincidence arrangement . .	Threefold	Fourfold	
Compensating absorber . .	170 g/cm² earth	204 g/cm² graphite (mass equivalent)	
Sidewise screening	no	no	yes

The layer of earth was a little less than the mass equivalent of air to compensate for the higher atomic number of earth with respect to air.

Contrary to expectation the percentage of the counts due to the soft component at sea level is not any larger than at 2000 m. Whereas Wick and collaborators assume that the differences to be expected on the decay hypothesis are covered up in the errors of measurement, the comparison with column C suggests the explanation that the counts at the greater

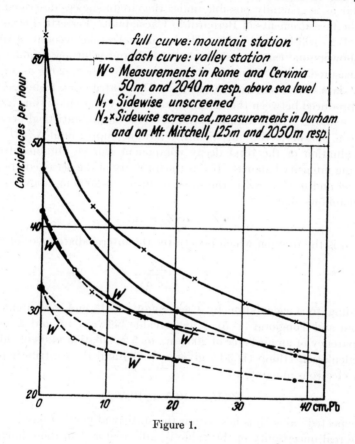

Figure 1.

heights are appreciably falsified by sidewise showers. That also agrees with the findings of Cocconi and Tongiorgi (C 5), according to whom the sidewise showers can amount to as much as 30% at 2000 m. even with fourfold coincidences. One remark in the paper (Nielsen, Ryerson, Nordheim and Morgan (N 5 and 6)) rejecting the assumption that sidewise showers are influential, probably concerns only the measurement of the hard component which was the real objective of their work. This is also in agreement with the measurements by Cocconi and Tongiorgi, who have established the fact that the influence of sidewise showers decreases as the thickness of the lead absorber is increased. The difference between the results in columns A and B of Table I may be attributed to the low precision of the measurements under B which served only as exploratory investigations. The deviations here are no greater than those between the individual measurements for which the mean value is given under A.

So far as is generally possible under the circumstances described above, only the measurements of Bernardini, Cacciapuoti, Ferretti, Piccioni, and Wick (B 9) will be used in the calculations. To take account of the side-wise showers one can in a somewhat rough and arbitrary manner reduce the measured values taken on the mountain by about 20% as suggested by the data of Cocconi and Tongiorgi. The contribution from decay electrons produced between the mountain and valley stations is thus $\Delta Z/M = 0.042 \pm 0.042$. After taking account of the mean statistical errors one, therefore, obtains as the statistically determined upper limit $\Delta Z/M = 0.10$. An evaluation of the total decay component can be obtained from the following intensity balance. If Z is the intensity of the decay component at sea level and if $Z' = \gamma Z$ is the same quantity at 2000 m. above sea level, then it follows that

$$Z = \alpha\gamma Z + \Delta Z \qquad (3)$$

where α is the fraction which penetrates the intermediate layer of air, and

$$Z = \frac{\Delta Z}{1 - \alpha\gamma}. \qquad (4)$$

According to a calculation by Cacciapuoti (C 1) and measurements by Cocconi and Tongiorgi (C 5), γ has a value between 1.5 and 2. For the transparency of an air layer of 2000 m., or 5.2 radiation units of thickness, our calculation (Bopp (B 30)) gives $\alpha = 0.3$ and the contribution of the decay electrons amounts to

$$Z/M = 10.5 \pm 10.5\%. \qquad (5)$$

The expected value thus lies within the statistical fluctuations.

The real uncertainty of the value is still greater than these fluctuations on account of the uncertainty in the approximations of the corrections. Probably the influence of the sidewise showers is still underestimated, since the measurements by Bernardini, Cacciapuoti, Ferretti, Piccioni, and Wick were made with only 3-fold coincidences. But a change in the other direction cannot be ruled out. In the latter case the Z and W components would not suffice to make up all of the particles of the soft component, and there must still be an appreciable primary residual R at sea level.

The observations of Wick and his collaborators, which were said to show qualitative proof of the existence of an appreciable R-component, are, on the basis of the foregoing remarks, no longer unconditionally conclusive. In the first place the fact that the Rossi curve taken at Cervinia under 170 g/cm.² of earth still shows a pronounced maximum can be explained, at least partially, by the unabsorbed fraction of the decay electrons. In the second place, the rapid rise with height of intensity of the soft component relative to that expected for the decay electrons can be tied up with the sidewise showers. Only the measurements by Cocconi and Tongiorgi (C 5) give results free from objections and showing a contribution of the R-component at sea level. These measurements show a decrease of the relative contribution of the soft component with increasing zenith angle at both 120 m. and 2200 m. above sea level, whereas the W and Z components must remain constant. The value of 6.5% computed from their measurements for the R-component is in agreement with Euler's estimates (E 5).

In summarizing, it can be stated that the foregoing actual determinations of the Z component do not contradict the values to be expected from the decay period of the meson. Yet the precision of measurement is so low that the presence of an appreciable contribution from primary electrons cannot be excluded, even at sea level. A direct determination of the primary residue is in agreement with the estimate of its intensity based upon the frequency of the large Hoffmann bursts. As the most probable values of the various contributions, we may write

$$Z/M = 18\%, \qquad W/M = 5\%, \qquad R/M = 6\%. \tag{6}$$

The first value can very well be too high.

10. THEORY OF THE MESON

By C. F. v. Weizsäcker, Strasbourg

1. Fundamentals

It is well known that as early as 1935 Yukawa (Y 2-6) postulated from nuclear physical considerations the existence of a particle which would have the same properties as those which now, on the basis of experiments, we ascribe to the meson. For the theoretical description of the meson we will, therefore, begin with Yukawa, and to this end we review briefly the status of nuclear physics as it was before Yukawa's theory.

The atomic nuclei, which consist only of protons and neutrons, can emit either electrons or positrons by β-decay. In order to clarify these facts the following elementary process is postulated: A neutron can transform itself, under suitable energy assumptions, into a proton and an electron, and conversely a proton can be transformed into a neutron and a positron. As a consequence of this process there should exist, according to Heisenberg, "exchange forces" between protons and neutrons. If a neutron in free space is transformed into a proton and an electron, then the electron can either go off into free space or unite again with the proton to form a neutron; but if there should be another proton in the vicinity of the original neutron, this can unite with the electron to form a neutron. Then, in this process, the original neutron becomes a proton, and the proton becomes a neutron. With this exchange of charge there must be associated a force field between the proton and the neutron. This is perhaps easiest to see if one thinks of the wave picture of the exchange electron rather than of the corpuscular. It can then be said: the neutron in its transformation excites a field, namely, the ψ-function of the electron, which now acts upon the neighboring proton. The most important qualitative distinction between this effect and the electromagnetic interaction of two charged particles consists in the fact that the interchange of charge behaves, as can be shown, in such a manner that the nuclear forces have the empirically required property of saturation.

This hypothesis was developed into a quantitative theory by Fermi in his theory of β-decay. Fermi assumed, as did Pauli in an older theory, that in β-decay there is emitted simultaneously with the electron an uncharged particle, called the "neutrino," which has the spin $1/2\hbar$ and obeys Fermi-statistics. In this manner he provided for the conservation of energy, angular momentum, and statistics in the decay process. Likewise, the β-decay process became amenable to quantum mechanical calculations. The field of the light weight particles, that is, the wave functions of the electron and neutrino, likewise gave a calculable interaction between the proton and neutron.

Unfortunately, however, this interaction was too small by a factor of the order of magnitude 10^{12}. This was not basically surprising because the postulated elementary process of β-decay is an extremely improbable process when thought of in terms of normal nuclear phenomena. The shortest known decay period of any β-radiator is of the order of one second, that is, about 10^{20} times longer than the time which a particle normally requires to traverse the nucleus. It is understandable that such a rare process should not result in an appreciable interaction.

In order to avoid these difficulties Yukawa retained the assumption of a special field for the nuclear forces but gave up the identification of the β-electrons with the particles associated with this field. Furthermore, he tried to fix up the properties of the field in such a way that they would yield the correct empirical values of the nuclear forces. Now, however, the β-decay remained unexplained. Hence Yukawa introduced the additional hypothesis that the "Quant" of the nuclear field, which we now call the meson, is itself unstable as regards disintegration into an electron and a neutrino. In this way a new constant of nature was brought in, namely the decay constant of the meson, which could be so chosen that the order of magnitude of the β-decay period would come out right. For review we list together the various processes, according to both theories, and designate the various particles as follows: P = proton, N = neutron, μ = meson, e = electron, ν = neutrino

		FERMI	YUKAWA
Exchange Force:	Initial state	$N + P$	$N + P$
	Intermediate state . .	$P + e + \nu + {}^-P$	$P + \mu + P$
	Final state	$P + N$	$P + N$
β-decay:	Initial state	N	N
	Intermediate state . .	—	$P + \mu$
	Final state	$P + e + \nu$	$P + e + \nu$

Since, according to Yukawa, the β-decay is a double process (1. creation of a meson, 2. decay of the meson) its small probability is conceivable without too extreme assumptions regarding the value of the meson decay period.

We still have to consider the question of the charge of the meson. Since in β-decay not only electrons but also positrons can be produced, there must be both positively and negatively charged mesons, as is also confirmed by the experiments with cosmic rays. To clarify nuclear forces one must also apparently postulate the existence of neutral mesons, for it is well known that the same force exists between two protons or between two neutrons as that between a proton and a neutron. If there were only charged mesons, the force between two protons could be explained only by a double exchange, in which each proton emits a meson and then absorbs the meson emitted by the other proton. In the usual approximate calculation of this kind of force field, any process is represented by an approximation of the same order as the number of elementary processes of which it may be thought to be composed; if the calculation is to converge, this double exchange process should take place less frequently than the single one and the empirical charge-independence of nuclear forces would be unexplained. However, we will show, a little further in the discussion, that the approximate calculations mentioned diverge and the conclusion is not assured. Yet it still remains remarkable that two essentially different processes should lead to exactly the same force. On the other hand, if one assumes the existence of neutral mesons these can lead naturally to a force between similar particles by a simple exchange: a proton emits a neutral meson and remains a proton—another proton absorbs the neutral meson.

The simplest assumption for the theory of nuclear forces would be that there are no charged but only neutral mesons. Thus the force between a proton and a neutron can be supplied by a neutral meson; the lack of dependence of nuclear forces on charge can be most simply explained if the carriers of the force field have no charge ("neutral theory"). Another possibility ("symmetric theory") is to ascribe to each particle an equal probability for the emission of charged and neutral mesons and then to choose the sign of the exchange energy so that, by suitable superposition of effects of the various kinds of mesons, the charge independence will again come out. The neutral theory, however, contradicts Yukawa's basic assumption since it again relinquishes the connection between β-decay and cosmic radiation. However, we will partially develop this theory in what follows as the simplest model of a meson theory from which the symmetrical theory departs in only a few additional details.

2. Scalar Theory

In order to come to quantitative statements, an assumption must be made about the field equations satisfied by the field of the nuclear forces. As the simplest equation we may consider the usual wave equation:

$$\Delta U - \frac{1}{c^2} \frac{\partial^2 U}{\partial t^2} = 0. \tag{1}$$

This equation must be valid in empty space, that is, in a space which contains only the nuclear field (or in other words only mesons) but, especially, no protons or neutrons, since these are sources of the nuclear field. If one extends the equation in the manner in which we develop it below in section 3, by equations which describe the interaction of mesons with protons and neutrons, then the field intensity U turns out to be the potential of the exchange forces produced by the mesons.

The spherically symmetrical solution of equation (1) with a singularity at the origin, which, therefore, should represent the nuclear field around a proton or neutron, is the well known Coulomb potential

$$U = \frac{\text{const}}{r}. \tag{2}$$

This potential, however, cannot be the right one since all characteristic properties of the nucleus (saturation, validity of the Coulomb law up to the nuclear boundary) show that the nuclear force falls off rapidly with distance. Equation (1) must, therefore, be altered. As the simplest alteration Yukawa chose the addition of a term proportional to U

$$\Delta U - \frac{1}{c^2}\frac{\partial^2 U}{\partial t^2} - \kappa^2 U = 0. \tag{3}$$

This equation has, as one can easily verify by substitution, the spherically symmetric solution

$$U = g^2 \frac{e^{-\kappa r}}{r}, \tag{4}$$

where g is an arbitrary constant. This potential law now has the desired property of short range. The experiments require that

$$\kappa^{-1} \approx 2 \cdot 10^{-13} \text{cm}. \tag{5}$$

What significance does this have for the physical properties of the nucleus?

In answer to this question we consider the particles associated with the field U. Equation (3) can be regarded as the relativistic Schrödinger equation (Klein-Gordon-equation) of the meson. If one writes the relativistic relation between energy and impulse in the form

$$-p^2 + \left(\frac{E}{c}\right)^2 - \mu^2 c^2 = 0, \tag{6}$$

and then replaces $\vec{p}$ and E, in accordance with the quantum mechanical prescription, by $\frac{\hbar}{i}$ grad and $-\frac{\hbar}{i}\frac{\partial}{\partial t}$, respectively, and divides by $\hbar^2$, and applies the operator thus formed to U, one obtains precisely the equation (3), where now

$$\kappa = \frac{\mu c}{\hbar} \tag{7}$$

Since μ is the rest mass of the particle considered, κ^{-1} is the Compton wave length of the meson. From (5) it follows that

$$\mu \approx 200 \text{ electron masses,} \tag{8}$$

a prediction which was confirmed by observations on the cosmic rays.

Nevertheless, the theory in the foregoing form still cannot be right. The experiments show, for example, that the potential depends strongly upon the relative spin orientation of the nuclear particles. A theory like the foregoing, which has only a scalar field intensity, cannot represent its directional dependence. We, therefore, present all available details of the vectorial form of the theory which is the most complete, at present.

3. Vectorial Theory

The constant changing over from one arbitrarily chosen wave equation to another might give rise to the impression that the theory consists only of *ad hoc* assumptions and contains exactly as many hypotheses as there are experimental facts to be explained. For such reasons, in fact, the theory at first received little attention, and it was all the more surprising when its fundamental concepts were brilliantly confirmed by cosmic ray experiments. In this regard we can throw some light on the situation by the remark that the freedom of choice of arbitrary wave equations is very much less than would at first appear. If the number of space components which the wave functions should have is established, then the various invariance requirements which the equation must satisfy allow only a very restricted choice of possibilities.

From the nature of the spin dependence of the nuclear forces, it follows that the field intensity must be at least a four-vector. Spin dependence of an exchange force means that in many cases not only the charge but also the spin of the proton and neutron are exchanged. Thus, if, for example, a neutron of spin $+ 1/2\hbar$ transforms itself into a proton and a meson, it must be possible that the proton remains with the spin $-1/2\hbar$; from the law for the conservation of angular momentum it follows that the meson must carry the spin $+ 1\hbar$. Since the exchange interaction is provided essentially by mesons for which the orbital momentum is zero the meson must have an actual spin of $+ 1\hbar$, analogous to the light quantum. A particle of this kind requires for its description in the wave picture at least a four vector to represent the field intensity (in the case of the light quantum this four vector is formed by the scalar and the vector potential). The analogy of the meson to the light quantum becomes still closer if one considers that the meson must have Bose-statistics in order that, in the conversion of the neutron into a proton and a meson, the statistical behavior remains unchanged.

We now choose from among the small number of possible equations which represent a meson of spin 1 the one which has the closest analogy to the Maxwell theory of light (Proca (P 7)). The meson field is described by four field components φ_1, φ_2, φ_3, φ_4, which together form a four vector. In analogy to the Maxwellian field we designate these as potentials and write (according to Bethe (B 13) and Jensen (J 5))

$$\left.\begin{aligned} \varphi_k &= \mathfrak{A}_k \\[2mm] \varphi_4 &= i\Phi, \end{aligned}\right\} \qquad (k = 1,2,3) \qquad (9)$$

in which $\mathfrak{A}$ corresponds to the vector potential, and Φ to the scalar potential. Confusion with the real electromagnetic field is not to be feared, for it never enters into our consideration. We further define (in the notation of Fröhlich, Heitler and Kemmer (F 4)) six quantities $\chi_{\alpha\beta}$ (greek indices run from 1 to 4, latin indices from 1 to 3) corresponding to the anti-symmetric tensor of the electric and magnetic field strength:

$$\left.\begin{aligned} \chi_{4k} &= i\mathfrak{E}_k, & \chi_{\alpha\alpha} &= 0, \\[2mm] \chi_{kl} &= \mathfrak{H}_m, \ (k \neq l \neq m) & \chi_{\alpha\beta} &= -\chi_{\beta\alpha}\,. \end{aligned}\right\} \qquad (10)$$

The connection between χ and φ is given by the defining equation:

$$\chi_{\alpha\beta} = \frac{\partial \varphi_\beta}{\partial x_\alpha} - \frac{\partial \varphi_\alpha}{\partial x_\beta} \qquad (11)$$

or, written out:

$$\left.\begin{aligned} \mathfrak{E} &= -\operatorname{grad}\Phi - \frac{\partial \mathfrak{A}}{c\,\partial t}, \\[2mm] \mathfrak{H} &= \operatorname{curl}\mathfrak{A}, \end{aligned}\right\} \qquad (12)$$

from which follow the first two Maxwellian equations

$$\left.\begin{aligned} \operatorname{curl}\mathfrak{E} + \frac{\partial \mathfrak{H}}{c\,\partial t} &= 0, \\[2mm] \operatorname{div}\mathfrak{H} &= 0. \end{aligned}\right\} \qquad (13)$$

In place of the other Maxwellian equations we write

$$\sum_\alpha \frac{\partial \chi_{\alpha\beta}}{\partial x_\alpha} = \kappa^2 \varphi_\beta \tag{14}$$

or, written out:

$$\left.\begin{array}{l} \operatorname{div} \mathfrak{E} + \kappa^2 \Phi = 0, \\[2mm] \operatorname{curl} \mathfrak{H} - \dfrac{\partial \mathfrak{E}}{c\,\partial t} + \kappa^2 \mathfrak{A} = 0. \end{array}\right\} \tag{15}$$

These equations differ from the Maxwellian by the term in κ^2. It may be remarked on the side that in this theory the Lorentz convention:

$$\sum_\beta \frac{\partial \varphi_\beta}{\partial x_\beta} = \operatorname{div} \mathfrak{A} + \frac{\partial \Phi}{c\,\partial t} = 0 \tag{16}$$

results immediately by differentiation of equation (14) with respect to χ_β. The physical meaning of the κ^2-term becomes most apparent if one substitutes for $\chi_{\alpha\beta}$ in (14) from (11) and takes account of (16):

$$\left.\begin{array}{l} \Delta\Phi - \dfrac{1}{c^2}\ddot\Phi - \kappa^2\Phi = 0, \\[2mm] \Delta\mathfrak{A} - \dfrac{1}{c^2}\ddot{\mathfrak{A}} - \kappa^2\mathfrak{A} = 0. \end{array}\right\} \tag{17}$$

That is, the Klein-Gordon equation holds for each of the four field components individually, and the κ^2 term expresses, as in the scalar theory, the existence of a rest mass of the meson.

The analogy with the theory of light is complete if one stipulates that all field components are real. Then the theory describes a single kind of particle and becomes adapted to the representation of neutral mesons. However, if φ and χ are allowed to be complex, and if along with equations (11) and (14) the conjugate complex quantities are included,

$$\chi_{\alpha\beta}^* = \frac{\partial \varphi_\beta^*}{\partial x_\alpha} - \frac{\partial \varphi_\alpha^*}{\partial x_\beta}, \tag{11*}$$

and

$$\sum_\alpha \frac{\partial \chi_{\alpha\beta}^*}{\partial x_\alpha} = \kappa^2 \varphi_\beta^*, \tag{14*}$$

then one has to a certain extent two independent sets of wave functions φ and φ^* and any linear combinations. The expression corresponding to the space density is then, as in the Klein-Gordon equation, no longer uniquely defined, and in this feature one can see, as Pauli and Weisskopf (P 1) have shown, a description of the emission of two kinds of particles with opposite charge. The complex theory, therefore, represents charged mesons.

4. Interaction with Nuclear Matter

The above equations represent the behavior of mesons in vacuum. For the treatment of their interaction with matter let us again start out from the analogy to the Maxwellian theory. Just as above, we constructed a "classical" theory of the meson field, that is, we overlooked the fact that the field intensities φ and χ are not ordinary numbers but are operators, so now we treat the interaction only in the classical approximation; at a later stage in the discussion the inherent (large) errors will be mentioned. At first the argument is limited to neutral mesons.

The electromagnetic field excited by a charge density ρ and a current density i may be calculated if one puts on the right side of (14) the four-vector with the components $4\pi\rho$, $4\pi i/c$. In the same way we should like to calculate the meson field excited by nuclear particles. Thus we make ρ proportional to the density expression $\psi^*\psi$ (ψ is the wave function of the nuclear particles), and i/c proportional to the associated current expression $\psi^*\vec{\alpha}\psi$. The proportionality factor g, having the dimensions of a charge, measures the strength of the meson-excited interaction between nuclear particles and meson field, just as in the radiation theory the elementary charge e measures the interaction of matter and radiation. (As a further factor for charged mesons an operator Q comes in which, for example in the excitation of a negative meson, changes the wave function of a neutron into that of a proton).

Since the forces are to be essentially dependent on spin, this statement, which is exactly analogous to the field excitation by purely electrical charges, is not at all satisfactory. However, we are free to add to equation (11) a six-vector which corresponds to the effect of a magnetic dipole (and an imaginary electrical dipole). The way in which a tensor of this kind is to be built up from wave functions by means of Dirac-matrices α, β and σ, is shown by the following formulae. Into these comes naturally a new proportionality factor f with the dimensions of a charge. Finally these equations read as follows

$$
\left.
\begin{aligned}
\operatorname{div} \mathfrak{E} + \kappa^2 \Phi &= 4\pi\rho, & \rho &= g\psi^*\psi, \\[2ex]
\operatorname{curl} \mathfrak{H} - \frac{\partial \mathfrak{E}}{c\,\partial t} + \kappa^2 \mathfrak{A} &= 4\pi\,\frac{i}{c}, & \frac{i}{c} &= g\psi^*\vec{\alpha}\psi, \\[2ex]
\mathfrak{E} + \operatorname{grad} \Phi + \frac{\partial \mathfrak{A}}{c\,\partial t} &= \frac{4\pi}{\kappa}\mathfrak{N}, & \mathfrak{N} &= if\psi^*\beta\vec{\alpha}\psi, \\[2ex]
\mathfrak{H} - \operatorname{curl} \mathfrak{A} &= \frac{4\pi}{\kappa}\mathfrak{M}, & \mathfrak{M} &= f\psi^*\beta\vec{\sigma}\psi.
\end{aligned}
\right\}
\tag{18}
$$

The reciprocal length κ must enter in the denominator of the last two equations in order that the factor f/κ may have the dimensions of a dipole moment. In the limiting case of the radiation theory, not only κ but also f/κ are equal to zero.

We now limit ourselves to non-relativistic effects for the heavy particles, i.e., to effects in which the matrix $\vec{\alpha}$, proportional to v/c, may be neglected. Then $\mathfrak{i}$ and $\mathfrak{N}$ disappear and, analogous to (17), we obtain

$$
\left.
\begin{aligned}
\Delta\Phi - \frac{1}{c^2}\ddot{\Phi} - \kappa^2\Phi &= -4\pi\rho, \\[2mm]
\Delta\mathfrak{A} - \frac{1}{c^2}\ddot{\mathfrak{A}} - \kappa^2\mathfrak{A} &= \frac{4\pi}{\kappa}\,\mathrm{curl}\,\mathfrak{M}.
\end{aligned}
\right\}
\tag{19}
$$

If a density distribution $\rho(\mathfrak{r})$ and a momentum distribution $\mathfrak{M}(\mathfrak{r})$ of the nuclear particles are assigned, one can solve the equations (19) analogously to the electrostatic case and obtain for the field distribution:

$$
\begin{aligned}
\Phi(\mathfrak{r}) &= \int d\tau'\,\frac{\rho(\mathfrak{r}')}{|\,\mathfrak{r}-\mathfrak{r}'\,|}\,e^{-\kappa\,\|\,\mathfrak{r}-\mathfrak{r}'\,\|} \approx \frac{g}{r}\,e^{-\kappa r}, \\[2mm]
\mathfrak{A}(\mathfrak{r}) &= -\frac{1}{\kappa}\int d\tau'\,\frac{\mathrm{curl}\,\mathfrak{M}(\mathfrak{r}')}{|\,\mathfrak{r}-\mathfrak{r}'\,|}\,e^{-\kappa\,\|\,\mathfrak{r}-\mathfrak{r}'\,\|} \approx -\frac{f}{\kappa}\,\mathrm{curl}\!\left(\mathfrak{s}\,\frac{e^{-\kappa r}}{r}\right).
\end{aligned}
\tag{20}
$$

Here the approximations given by the expressions at the extreme right refer to distances r from the exciting nuclear particle, which are large compared with the space in which ρ and $\mathfrak{M}$ differ appreciably from zero. Furthermore, the mean moment vector of the nuclear particle is

$$
\mathfrak{s} = \int \psi^*\beta\,\vec{\sigma}\psi\,d\tau' \approx \int \psi^*\,\vec{\sigma}\psi\,d\tau'
\tag{21}
$$

If we now seek the force which a nuclear particle exerts on another nuclear particle by means of the meson field, in the statistical approximation to which we here confine ourselves we can eliminate the meson field entirely and reckon only with a potential energy dependent upon the position and spin of the heavy particles. In order to calculate this we first need the expression for the interaction energy between nuclear particles and the matter-field. It can be derived in a fashion exactly analogous to the procedure in the Maxwellian Theory (cf. Bethe) and is given by

$$
H = \int d\tau\left\{\rho\Phi - \frac{1}{c}(\mathfrak{i}\mathfrak{A}) + \frac{1}{\kappa}(\mathfrak{M}\mathfrak{H}) - \frac{1}{\kappa}(\mathfrak{N}\mathfrak{E})\right\}.
\tag{22}
$$

we skip over the derivation; the two terms important for our purposes are self explanatory, the first term of the integrand $\rho\Phi$ (i.e. the energy density) by electrostatic and the third term $1/\kappa(\mathfrak{M}\mathfrak{H})$ by magnetostatic analogy.

If a field $\mathfrak{E}_1, \mathfrak{H}_1$ excited by particle 1 acts upon a particle 2, then, (if $r = |\, \mathfrak{r}_1 - \mathfrak{r}_2 \,|$)

$$E_{\text{pot}} = \frac{g_1 g_2}{r}\, e^{-\kappa r} + \frac{1}{\kappa}\, (\mathfrak{M}_2 \mathfrak{H}_1(\mathfrak{r}_2)), \tag{23}$$

in which

$$\mathfrak{H}_1(\mathfrak{r}_2) = \frac{4\pi}{\kappa}\, \mathfrak{M}_1(\mathfrak{r}_2) - \operatorname{curl} \mathfrak{A}_1(\mathfrak{r}_2). \tag{24}$$

Expanding (24) we finally get:

$$\left.\begin{aligned}
E_{\text{pot}} &= U + V_1 + V_2\,, \\[1em]
U &= g_1 \mathring{g}_2\, \frac{e^{-\kappa r}}{r}, \\[1em]
V_1 &= \frac{2}{3}\, f_1 f_2 (\mathfrak{s}_1 \mathfrak{s}_2)\, \frac{e^{-\kappa r}}{r}, \\[1em]
V_2 &= f_1 f_2\, \frac{e^{-\kappa r}}{r}\left(\frac{1}{\kappa^2 r^2} + \frac{1}{\kappa r} + \frac{1}{3}\right)\!\left(-3\,\frac{(\mathfrak{s}_1 \mathfrak{r})(\mathfrak{s}_2 \mathfrak{r})}{r^2} + (\mathfrak{s}_1 \mathfrak{s}_2)\right).
\end{aligned}\right\} \tag{25}$$

This potential has one very disadvantageous property. The expression V_2 contains terms which at $r = 0$ diverge like $1/r^3$ and $1/r^2$. Whereas a divergence like $1/r$ (Coulomb field) is well known to present no difficulties quantum mechanically, no stationary states exist in a potential which diverges more strongly than $1/r^2$. The reason for this can be easily explained on the basis of the indetermination principle. If a particle is restricted by means of a potential to a space of approximate diameter r, then it possesses an undetermined momentum of the order of magnitude $\hbar/r$ and hence a kinetic energy which is proportional to $1/r^2$. If now as r becomes smaller the potential energy increases less rapidly than $1/r^2$, then there must be a value of r at which the kinetic energy exceeds the potential energy; thus, if the particle were to be limited to a still smaller space, it could not be held by the potential. This critical value of r gives approximately the extension of the wave function in the lowest stationary state. If the potential energy increases more rapidly than $1/r^2$, it gets larger and larger in comparison with the kinetic energy as the distance is reduced; thus the particles must approach one another closer and closer without limit (with radiation of the kinetic energy acquired by acceleration), and there exists, in general, no lowest stationary state. The empirical existence of nuclei with a fixed radius, therefore, shows that (25) cannot represent the correct potential.

This difficulty is not accidental. Furthermore, it is bound up with the fundamental problem of any theory of this kind, as we remark at the end of the chapter. Many times, however, one has had the hope that the results of the theory would be right for sufficiently great particle distances, and in the hope of a future rectification of the process the potential has been cut off at a definite small distance. The consequences of a process of this kind are treated in following chapter by Flügge.

We now evaluate the absolute magnitude of the force constant. κ has already been determined in Section 2 from the range of the nuclear forces. g and f must follow from the strength of the nuclear forces. The determination is admittedly very inaccurate, since, with the diverging potential, one can get any value he pleases for the binding energy of the atomic nucleus, regardless of the value of the force constant; it is required only to make a suitable choice of the radius at which the potential is cut off. The determination becomes possible, however, if one also takes account of the size of the nucleus. If, for example, a very small force constant is chosen, then it is necessary to go to very small radii to obtain sufficient binding. The eigenfunctions of the particles bound by this force will differ from zero only over distances of the order of magnitude of this small cut-off radius. It is, therefore, necessary to demand that the cut-off radius be not much smaller than the radius of a light weight nucleus; in this way a condition is placed upon g and f. In the special case where it is assumed that $g = 0$ (Flügge remarks on this hypothesis of Bethe's in Chapt. 11) it results that

$$\frac{f^2}{\hbar c} \approx 0.08. \tag{26}$$

f is then about three times greater than the elementary electric charge e ($e^2/\hbar c = 0.0073$).

5. Theory of β-decay

The theory of β-decay is important because it provides a means of calculating from the observed periods of β-decay the mean life of the meson which can then be compared with the results obtained from cosmic ray experiments. The fundamentals of the calculation are outlined below according to the method of Bethe and Nordheim (B 18).

The interaction of the meson with light-weight particles (electrons and neutrinos) can be dealt with in a manner analogous to the treatment of their interaction with heavy particles (protons and neutrons). In β-decay a meson is emitted from the heavy particle by a process in which a neutron disappears and simultaneously a proton is created; then similarly this meson is absorbed by the light weight particles with the creation of an electron and a neutrino. Formally, the analogy can be made even closer. If the neutrino is treated by the Dirac equation, then, just as the positron is related to the electron, so there is a counterpart to the neutrino called the antineutrino. Just as the creation of a positron is described as the disappearance of an electron of negative energy, so also the creation of the antineutrino is represented as the cancellation of a neutrino. Because of the symmetry of emission and absorption the same interaction which allows for the simultaneous creation of a neutrino and an electron can also allow for their simultaneous disappearance. The latter is equivalent to the creation of an antineutrino and a positron. This is the way the positron decay is described in the Fermi theory of β-decay. Now, moreover, we have a free hand in deciding which of the two kinds of neutrinos shall be designated the neutrino and which the antineutrino, and it has been agreed to call the particle created simultaneously with the positron the neutrino. It may be noted that, formally, the number of light-weight particles remains constant: when a neutrino appears, an electron of negative energy disappears; when an electron appears, a neutrino of negative energy disappears. β-decay can then be briefly described as follows: A neutron is converted into a proton with the emission of a meson, and a neutrino of negative energy is converted into an electron with the absorption of the same meson.

This ability of the light-weight particles to emit and absorb mesons is taken into account, in equation (18), by adding to the density-current vectors ρ, i and to the momentum tensors $\mathfrak{N}$, $\mathfrak{M}$ which were excited by the heavy particles, similar quantities arising from the light-weight particles. The charge must also be taken into account and we write:

$$\rho_s = g\psi^* Q_s\psi, \qquad\qquad i_s = cg\psi^* \vec{\alpha}Q_s\psi, \left.\begin{array}{c} \\ \\ \\ \end{array}\right\}$$
$$\mathfrak{M}_s = f\psi^*\beta\ \vec{\sigma}Q_s\psi, \qquad\qquad \mathfrak{N}_s = if\psi^*\beta\ \vec{\alpha}Q_s\psi. \quad (27\text{a})$$

Here Q is an operator which transforms the eigenfunction of a neutron into that of a proton and visa versa. In exact analogy we write for the light-weight particles whose wave function may be designated by χ

$$\rho_l = G\chi^* Q_l\chi, \qquad\qquad i_l = cG\chi^* \vec{\alpha}Q_l\chi, \left.\begin{array}{c} \\ \\ \\ \end{array}\right\}$$
$$\mathfrak{M}_l = F\chi^*\beta\ \vec{\sigma}Q_l\chi, \qquad\qquad \mathfrak{N}_l = iF\chi^*\beta\ \vec{\alpha}Q\chi. \quad (27\text{b})$$

F and G are new constants which measure the decay probability of the meson. The expressions which went into equation (18) are now to be replaced by the sum of the corresponding expressions from (26) and (27):

$$\rho = \rho_s + \rho_l \text{ etc.} \qquad (27\text{c})$$

If, on the one hand, we work out the mean life of a free meson, which is approximately known from the cosmic rays, and, on the other hand, we derive the mean life of a familiar β-radiator, we will obtain two independent predictions of the constants F and G; in this way we can test the theory.

One of the solutions of equation (12) and (15) corresponds to a plane wave in the theory of light and represents the free meson. With this and with the wave functions of the free electron and of the antineutrino, the matrix element H_{nm} of the potential energy (22) can be evaluated, corresponding to the transition from the free meson to the electron and antineutrino; from this one gets the decay period τ_μ of the free meson according to the well known formula.

$$\frac{1}{\tau_\mu} = \frac{2\pi}{\hbar} \mid H_{nm} \mid^2 \sigma, \tag{28}$$

where σ is the number of possible final states per energy interval. This becomes

$$\frac{1}{\tau_\mu} = \frac{\mu c^2}{\hbar}\left(\frac{2}{3}\frac{G^2}{\hbar c} + \frac{1}{3}\frac{F^2}{\hbar c}\right). \tag{29}$$

The β-decay of a neutron in a nucleus is calculated like the exchange force in the preceding section, with the only exception that now the mesons emitted by the heavy particles are absorbed by the light-weight ones. In the Hamiltonian function (22) the symmetrical form $\frac{1}{2}(\rho_s\Phi_l + \rho_l\Phi_s)$ is to be substituted for $\rho\Phi$, and similar procedures are to be used for the other terms; here Φ_s is the meson field excited by the heavy particles, and Φ_l is that excited by the light-weight particles. If we again neglect i_s and $\mathfrak{N}_s$, a formula exactly analogous to (25) is obtained (except that now the assumption is not made as it was there that the density distribution of the two kinds of particles is nearly in the form of a point, and hence the spatial integration is not carried out):

$$
\left.
\begin{aligned}
H = \iint \frac{e^{-\kappa r}}{r}\rho_s\rho_l d\tau_s d\tau_l + \\
+ \iint \frac{e^{-\kappa r}}{r}\left[\frac{2}{3}(\mathfrak{M}_s\mathfrak{M}_l) + \left\{3\frac{(\mathfrak{M}_s r)(\mathfrak{M}_l r)}{r^2} - (\mathfrak{M}_s\mathfrak{M}_l)\right\}\right. \\
\left.\left\{\frac{1}{\kappa^2 r^2} + \frac{1}{\kappa r} + \frac{1}{3}\right\}d\tau_s d\tau_l\right].
\end{aligned}
\right\} \tag{30}
$$

Since the wave length of the created light-weight particle is large compared with the nuclear dimensions, or the region within which ρ_s and $\mathfrak{M}_s$ differ appreciably from zero, it is permissible to replace the wave functions of the light-weight particles by constant values χ_s and χ_ν. With

$$\int \frac{e^{-\kappa r}}{r}d\tau = \frac{4\pi}{\kappa^2} \tag{31}$$

it follows that

$$H = \frac{4\pi}{\kappa^2} \int \{gG\chi_c^* \chi_\nu \psi_P^* \psi_N + \tfrac{2}{3}fF(\chi_c^* \beta \, \vec{\sigma} \chi_\nu) \psi_P^* \beta \, \vec{\sigma} \psi_N)\} d\tau. \qquad (32)$$

The first term of the integrand is the exact equivalent of Fermi's hypothesis; only by the appearance of two constants g and G is it evident that in the process two transition probabilities are involved. The second term effects a β-transition in which the spin of the heavy particle can flop over in the manner discussed by Gamov and Teller (G 1).

We compare the theory with experiment. The systematization of the β-decay of light nuclei (Grönblom (G 10)) requires that spin reversals take place in β-decay. In particular, the simplest well known β-radiator He^6 cannot decay without spin reversal since we have to ascribe the spin 0 to He^6 and the spin 1 to the product nucleus Li^6. Moreover, a spin reversal in a transition forbidden in the first approximation is also possible with the purely Fermi interaction, if the light-weight particles have an orbital momentum. However, the decay of the He^6 is too rapid to warrant its being regarded as forbidden. At any rate, we shall not obtain too short a decay period of the meson if we treat the constant F as though it alone were responsible for the decay of He^6 $(G = 0)$ and likewise treat the constant f as though it alone were responsible for the nuclear forces $(g = 0$, cf. the preceding section) and introduce these constants into equation (29). Thus it follows that $F^2/\hbar c \approx 10^{-18}$ and $\tau_\mu \approx 10^{-8}$ sec. This is to be compared with the value $\tau_\mu = 1$ to $2 \cdot 10^{-6}$ sec. determined from the cosmic radiation.

The agreement of the two numbers is rather poor but perhaps better than would be obtained by pure accident. Let us picture to ourselves, qualitatively, the meaning of the above calculation. The normal β-radiators have decay periods which extend down only to values of the order of a few seconds. The decay period of the meson in the theory of Yukawa must be shorter for two reasons. First, the meson decays immediately whereas a β-radiator has first to excite a meson which then decays. (Since the mass of the meson is so great that its excitation is not possible, consistent with the law for the conservation of energy, it can obviously be excited only to a virtual intermediate state; in other words, each excitation can last for such a short period of time that the energy of the system can be determined, according to the relation of the indeterminacy principle $\Delta E \cdot \Delta t \geq \hbar$ only to an accuracy of the order of the rest energy of the meson). The fact that $f^2/\hbar c$ is of the order of magnitude $1/10$, hence not much smaller than 1, means, moreover, that the meson is excited very frequently; hence this reason for a shorter decay period of the meson is not very important. The second reason lies in the large rest mass of the meson which gives the light-weight particles a disintegration energy of nearly 100 million volts. There is the well known Sargent relation between energy and decay period of the β-radiator, according to which a nucleus giving a β-ray of this energy, should have a decay period of the order of that found for the meson. The Yukawa arrangement of the meson in the series of β-radiators is, therefore, consistent with the experiments within the limits of accuracy with which the Sargent relation can be extrapolated to such high energies.

The above calculation is in a sense an attempt to carry out this extrapolation quantitatively on the basis of the theoretical interpretation which Fermi has already given to the Sargent relation. In view of the factor 100 which separates the two values of τ_μ, this attempt is regarded as unsuccessful. The Yukawa theory in this application, as well as in the case of nuclear forces, is thus apparently in qualitative agreement with experiments, but, in its present form, it is unsuited to quantitative deductions.

6. Scattering of Mesons on Nuclear Particles

For the understanding of the passage of mesons through the atmosphere it is important to decide how strongly they are scattered. If no forces act between the meson and electron other than those considered in the section on β-decay, the scattering on electrons can be neglected (cf. also Section 7 and the 7th Chapter on burst excitation by mesons). The scattering on nuclear particles can be accurately calculated from the theory just as the scattering of light by electrons is calculated. One obtains for the effective cross-section of scattering

$$Q = \text{const} \frac{1}{\kappa^4} \frac{p^4}{E^2}, \tag{33}$$

where p is the momentum and E is the energy of the meson. The constant is independent of the proton mass and larger than can be reconciled with the experiments. The expression differs from the effective cross-section for the scattering of light quanta on electrons in that it finally increases quadratically with increasing energy and that it has a finite value, even for infinitely heavy protons, because of its independence of the proton mass. The latter is very surprising when it is recalled that the scattering takes place only by the sympathetic vibration of the scattering particle under the influence of the incident wave, and hence should vanish with infinite inertia of the scattering particle.

The explanation, according to Heisenberg (H 2), lies in the fact that it is not the center of mass of the proton which gives rise, by its vibrations, to the scattering, but rather the two inertia-less degrees of freedom, namely the spin and the "charge coordinate" (the freedom to be either a proton or a neutron). The scattering, therefore, comes in through the f-terms which do not appear in electrodynamics. Now the calculated scattering is certainly not to be reconciled with the experiments, and we, therefore, have a third proof of the breakdown of the theory in answering quantitative questions. We now turn to the fundamental difficulties concealed in these failures.

7. Discussion of the Difficulties

The difficulty of the divergence of the potential at small distances, like that of the large scattering cross-section, can be summarized in the statement: The theory breaks down if mesons of too large a momentum are involved. Now, the exchange interaction between two heavy particles at a given separation r is produced essentially by mesons with wave length of the order of r and with momentum of the order $\hbar/r$. The difficulties, therefore, mean that the theory breaks down for a certain high momentum or, what amounts to the same thing, for a certain small distance.

However, a theory can be formulated, as Möller and Rosenfeld (M 5) have shown, through the use of additional field quantities with other relativistic transformation properties, in which the divergent potential terms do not enter. There are other deep-seated divergence difficulties, which remain even in this formulation of the theory and render it of questionable value for giving the desired result. These divergences result if one goes over from the classical proximation theory, which we have thusfar presented, to a rigorous quantum theoretical calculation.

The presentation of the theory given above treats the meson as a field propagated continuously in space. It, therefore, deviates completely from the fundamental experimental fact that the meson appears in reality as a single particle. According to the general rules of the quantum theory, the particle properties of matter are taken into account if one starts out with the wave picture by treating the field quantities not as ordinary numbers but as operators. The pertinent mathematical formalities will not be presented here, but we will attempt to describe intuitively the most important of its consequences. In the quantum theory it is customary to start out with the field equations in empty space, just as we did above in the classical theory, and then to introduce the terms which give the interactions between the various kinds of particles as perturbations. The results of the calculations, for example for the potential of the exchange forces, have the form of a power series in the interaction constants g and f, of which the first term is that calculated above. The higher order terms, however, are by no means small. In the first place, the dimensionless constant $f^2/\hbar c$, which functions here as the parameter for the expansion, analogous to the fine structure constant of electrodynamics, is not very small compared to unity. And, secondly, the coefficients of the higher order terms, analogous to the self-energy terms in electrodynamics, are large and in some cases infinite.

What physical processes correspond to the higher order terms of the expansion? In the case of the exchange forces the first term is the interaction through which one meson is emitted and absorbed; the second term arises from the simultaneous emission and reabsorption of two mesons, etc. The failure of the expansion to converge, therefore, means that in the process considered many mesons are frequently created in one elementary act. Heisenberg (H 2) has shown that this takes place as soon as very small distances (of the order of $1/\kappa$), or high momenta, come into play. Now there is the question whether this kind of "explosive shower" is actually to be expected in nature. From the theoretical standpoint two opposite views have been advanced. Evidently the theory cannot be right as long as divergent terms appear in it. Since the multiple processes described are associated with the divergent expressions, American authors, especially, have conjectured as to a correct (but unknown) form of the theory which would contain no divergences and in which the multiple processes would not occur or, at least, only with extreme rarity. This view, however, does not say how the divergences are to be made to disappear, and Heisenberg is of the contrary opinion, that the theory can free itself of the divergences only along the line of a correct description of the multiple processes. If one knows that multiple processes occur predominantly, it is inconsistent with the facts to start out with a description of the phenomenon in which the creation of each individual new particle is regarded as a small perturbation; it is not to be wondered that divergences occur in this formulation.

The exact meaning of the latter view may be illustrated by an example. Heisenberg has formulated the conditions for the applicability of the present quantum theory: in the process considered the momentum transferred in the coordinate system in which the center of mass of the physical structure in question is at rest must be less than μc (μ = mass of the meson), or in any arbitrary coordinate system the energy transfer E and momentum transfer p must satisfy the condition

$$p^2 - \frac{E^2}{c^2} < \mu^2 c^2. \tag{34}$$

Otherwise there would be a high probability for the simultaneous creation of many mesons, a situation which is contrary to the conditions for the applicability of the usual quantum theoretical methods (and also of the divergences occurring in them). On the other hand, Oppenheimer and Snyder have objected that in the special problem of the excitation of secondary electrons by mesons (cf. Chapt. 7 on the burst-excitation by mesons) the calculation must break down on this condition even for primary energies of the meson of 10^{10} eV, whereas the interaction terms become large enough for one to expect a failure of the approximation only at 10^{12} eV; the extension of the range of validity of the formula up to 10^{12} eV is in agreement with the experiments. Oppenheimer and Snyder are, therefore, of the opinion that it is not the appearance of small distances (or high momenta) but rather the amount of the interaction energy, which places the limit on the theories thus far proposed. The reply to this, according to Heisenberg, is that the formula may well remain valid up to 10^{12} eV but that it will then no longer mean what it meant in the sense of the calculations used in its derivation: namely, the probability that a meson excites one secondary electron and nothing more. It is more likely from the large transfer of momentum that several mesons will also be excited simultaneously with the secondary electron. This is exactly analogous with the result of Bloch and Nordsieck (B 27), who have shown that the usual formula for the Rutherford scattering cross-section of electrons on charged particles does not give the probability that the electron will be scattered and that nothing else will happen, but rather that the electron will be scattered and simultaneously a certain number of light quanta will be emitted.

All of these questions can be decided only if we possess a quantitative theory of these processes. An approximation procedure proposed by Heisenberg for their treatment will not be presented here, but we will limit ourselves to a qualitative discussion of the previously mentioned difficulties from the point of view currently adopted.

It is of no concern that, at small distances from the nuclear particle, the expression for the exchange force diverges too strongly in the first approximation, calculated above, since the higher approximations in that calculation diverge much more strongly. The attempt has been made to use the expression for the potential at large distances and to cut it off at small distances. However, the expression so derived should have no quantitative significance since apparently there is no experiment in which the potential can be tested at large distances independently of its behavior at small distances. For the calculation of stationary states this is self evident; for, since, without the cutoff, there is no stationary state, the position of the stationary states depend entirely upon the nature of the cutoff. Moreover, collision experiments, e.g., those in which the deflection of a nuclear particle is measured when it passes by another similar particle at a sufficiently large given distance, are fundamentally unsuited to this purpose, especially on account of the exponential drop of potential at great distances. If we wish to be sure that the passing particle does not approach arbitrarily close to the other, we must localize it in space and thereby renounce an arbitrary precision in the knowledge of its momentum. If, however, the change of momentum experienced by a particle in its passage, because of the exchange force, is less than the error thus imposed upon our original knowledge of the momentum, obviously no knowledge of the potential can be gained by this experiment.

We demonstrate this generalization by a rough calculation. We allow one nuclear particle to fly past another at a distance r. In order to be sure that it does not fly past at distance 0, its position in space must be known with an uncertainty $\Delta q < r$, and the uncertainty in its momentum is

$$\Delta p > \frac{\hbar}{r}. \tag{35}$$

This relation applies to the momentum perpendicular to the direction of motion. In the direction of motion its velocity must be so great that during the collision time, that is, the time to travel the distance AB

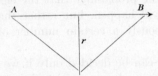

which is of the order r/v, the sidewise displacement, because of the uncertainty in momentum cited above, should remain smaller than r. The unknown component of velocity perpendicular to the direction of motion is $\Delta p/M$, and, therefore, it must follow that

$$\frac{\Delta p}{M} \cdot \frac{r}{v} < r \tag{36}$$

or

$$v > \frac{\Delta p}{M} = \frac{\hbar}{Mr} \tag{37}$$

The momentum p transferred during the collision time is now to be compared with Δp. It is about equal to the average force acting during this time multiplied by the collision time, or

$$p \approx -\frac{\partial U}{\partial r} \cdot \frac{r}{v} = \frac{g^2 \kappa e^{-\kappa r}}{v}, \tag{38}$$

where for the sake of simplicity the static potential U is introduced and $1/r$ is neglected in comparison with κ; in other words it is assumed that the collision distance is large compared to the Compton wavelength of the meson at which distance this law of force begins to be in error. From (35) and (38) it follows that

$$\frac{p}{\Delta p} \lesssim \frac{g^2}{\hbar c} \cdot \frac{c}{v} \, \kappa r e^{-\kappa r}. \tag{39}$$

In the limiting case of very large distances, because of the exponential fall of potential, the momentum transfer is small compared with the uncertainty of the momentum. The ratio is most favorable when r is nearly equal to $1/\kappa$. In order for $p/\Delta p$ to become greater than unity, since $g^2/\hbar c \approx 1/10$ we must have $v \lesssim c/30$. On the other hand, (37) requires that

$$v > \frac{\hbar}{M} \cdot \frac{\mu c}{\hbar} = \frac{\mu}{M} c \approx \frac{c}{10}, \tag{40}$$

so that the two conditions for v are mutually inconsistent in the most favorable calculation.

The conditions (37) and (39) may be combined in the condition

$$\frac{g^2}{\hbar c} \frac{M}{\mu} \gg 1. \tag{41}$$

Since we must postulate that $g^2/\hbar c < 1$ if the theoretical separation into heavy particle and meson fields, from which we started out, is to have any sense, then the only way to have a measurable field in an abstract theory would be to increase the mass ratio of proton and meson. In this manner the actual impossibility of a classical meson theory is tied up with the empirical fact that to measure the meson field there are no elementary particles of greater rest mass than the proton.

What can now be conjectured about the nature of the deviations of the actual force from that just calculated. It would be difficult to represent the actual force by a potential dependent upon the coordinates of two particles. The simultaneous emission and absorption of several mesons, leading to the correction of the law of force, must not be limited to *two* nuclear particles. For example, if several mesons can be created from a single nuclear particle, these will be absorbed by several other nuclear particles. This kind of process must lead to forces which depend upon the coordinates of several particles so that the force between a proton and a neutron depends upon the simultaneous position of all other neighboring nuclear particles. The experiments of nuclear physics (for example the binding energy of He^5) point, in fact, in this direction, (cf. especially H. Primakoff and T. Hostein (P 8)).

Another consequence of the strong interaction would be the existence of higher states of the proton and neutron in which the particle is doubly charged, triply charged, etc. Wentzel (W 5) has suggested this. The additional charge can be ascribed to the surrounding meson field. The experiments, to be sure, have not revealed this kind of structure.

Finally, as Heisenberg has shown, the meson scattering on nuclear particles will be essentially reduced if account is taken of the fact that the two inertialess degrees of freedom of the nuclear particle have, in consequence of the virtual emission and reabsorption of mesons, a strong "self-field" which invests their oscillations with an inertia in the same way that the electromagnetic self-field of a charge produces rest mass.

11. MESON THEORY OF THE DEUTERON

By S. Flügge, Berlin

An attempt was made in 1940 by Bethe (B 13, 14) to arrive at a quantitative formulation of the meson theory free from all objections. The basic idea of this attempt was the following: If the interaction force between two nuclear particles is produced by the meson field, then the empirically known measurable quantities, which are the consequence of this interaction, should also be representable quantitatively by the theory of the meson. Such measurable quantities in the systems resulting from two nuclear particles are:

1. The mass defect of the deuteron in the ground state, or the binding energy between proton and neutron with parallel spins.

2. The binding energy of the state in which the two nuclear particles have opposite spins. The latter is determined from scattering experiments and turns out to be, quantitatively, the same for the systems proton-neutron (the first excitation state of the deuteron) and proton-proton.

3. The quadrupole moment of the deuteron in the ground state, which arises from the fact that the electrical charge distribution is not spherically symmetrical about the center of mass but is somewhat elongated. The existence of a quadrupole moment shows that the neutron-proton force must contain a spin-orbit coupling term. As a matter of fact, a term of this kind comes naturally into the meson theory, in contrast to the older and more arbitrary statement of Majorana and Heisenberg for the nuclear forces.

It must be regarded as fundamentally futile to attempt to derive these three quantities quantitatively from the meson theory, and in this manner to find what assumptions have to be made to tie the theory down on questions which cannot be resolved from more general points of view, for instance, by invariance arguments. This difficulty is not very surprising when one reviews the arguments of the previous chapter. However, the presentation of these attempts should not be skipped over completely since it is an interesting example of the application of the meson theory, and it always aids the understanding to consider in a concrete case the unraveling of the difficulties, the general antecedents of which have already been realized from fundamental arguments.

It has already been pointed out in the previous article that there are two possibilities for the meson theory:

a) **Neutral theory.** In this case an uncharged meson is introduced. Consequently, there is no difference between the proton and neutron as regards the force of interaction provided by the exchange of a meson between the two nuclear particles, a fact which agrees with the second experimental observation cited above. It has been shown that this neutral theory, with the introduction of certain cut-off rules, is also suitable to represent the other two experimental observations on the deuteron. On the other hand, it has proved fundamentally unsuited for the explanation of β-decay since it allows no room for the transformation of a proton into a neutron and vice versa. For this reason alone it certainly cannot contain the whole truth.

b) **Symmetrical theory.** In order to explain the β-decay we must introduce charged mesons of both signs. But then only those processes can be understood in which a proton transforms into a neutron and vice versa. In this theory forces exist only between proton and neutron, and there is no interaction force between similar nuclear particles, a fact which contradicts the second experimental observation (scattering of protons on protons). In order to represent these observations and the β-decay at the same time, it is necessary to introduce both charged *and* uncharged mesons. Since the proton-neutron force agrees quantitatively with the proton-proton force, it is necessary to ascribe to both nuclear particles the same emission probability and the same absorption probability for the charged as for the uncharged mesons. It will be shown that a symmetrical theory of this kind is not adequate to represent the properties of the deuteron quantitatively. Thus this manner of reasoning can at most contain only a part of the truth.

The mathematical formulation for the force of interaction between two nuclear particles resulting from the neutral theory has already been carried out in the foregoing chapter. As a result the potential energy of the interaction of two nuclear particles at a distance r from one another is

$$V = U + V_1 + V_2$$

with

$$U = g^2 \frac{e^{-\kappa r}}{r},$$

$$V_1 = \frac{2}{3} f^2 (\vec{\sigma}_1 \cdot \vec{\sigma}_2) \frac{e^{-\kappa r}}{r},$$

$$V_2 = f^2 \left(-3 \frac{(\vec{\sigma}_1 \cdot \mathfrak{r})(\vec{\sigma}_2 \cdot \mathfrak{r})}{r^2} + (\vec{\sigma}_1 \cdot \vec{\sigma}_2) \right) \frac{e^{-\kappa r}}{r} \left(\frac{1}{3} + \frac{1}{\kappa r} + \frac{1}{\kappa^2 r^2} \right).$$

The first two terms U and V_1 correspond to central forces; here only the intensity of the force is dependent upon the spin $\vec{\sigma}_1$ and $\vec{\sigma}_2$ of the two particles. The third term V_2, which is also represented as a "Tensor force", contains the spin-orbit coupling produced by the electric quadrupole moment.

The symmetrical theory requires in its formulation the concept of a difference between proton and neutron. Actually, this difference is realized by introducing the charge as another quantum number which can take on two values and, therefore, can be treated exactly like the spin. Hence, to every nuclear particle five degrees of freedom are ascribed, three for the motion in space, one for the spin, and one for the charge.

The exact mathematical explanation of this method will be passed over here. One proceeds by introducing the "charge operator" $\vec{\tau}$ analogous to the spin operator $\vec{\sigma}$; the potential energy then takes the form

$$V = (U + V_1 + V_2) \cdot (\vec{\tau}_1 \cdot \vec{\tau}_2).$$

Without referring to the symbolism we can express the essential facts in the following manner: Since, according to the Pauli principle, only those states exist which are antimetric with respect to the exchange of two particles, or in this case of two variable-quintuplets, the states can be grouped in the following manner.

Table 1.

Spectroscopic notation	Position	Spin	Charge	$(\vec{\tau}_1 \vec{\tau}_2)$	Example
^3S, ^3D . . .	symmetr.	symmetr.	antimetr.	-3	Ground state of the deuteron
^1S, ^1D . . .	symmetr.	antimetr.	symmetr.	$+1$	Excited deuteron
^3P	antimetr.	symmetr.	symmetr.	$+1$	
^1P	antimetr.	antimetr.	antimetr.	-3	

We have, accordingly, to introduce the potential energy $-3V$ for the ground state and $+V$ for the excited state.

For the *quantitative* solution, or, essentially, for the solution of the Schrödinger equation with the potential function given, Bethe has introduced a simplification by putting $g = 0$, thus omitting the term U. This term was interpreted in the neutral theory, as well as for the excited state in the symmetrical theory, as an additional repulsion, and for the ground state in the symmetrical theory, as an attraction. The omission is purely arbitrary and is based only upon the heuristic argument of greater simplicity ("single force hypothesis").

Furthermore, it has proved to be necessary to cut off the potential V at a certain radius r_0 in order to avoid the divergence difficulties at $r = 0$ arising from the term V_2. These difficulties have already been discussed in the foregoing chapter; here is one of the principal causes of failure of Bethe's attempt. For the cut-off two different prescriptions were used; in the first prescription the rule was that $V = 0$ for $r < r_0$, in the second it was assumed that in the same range $V = V(r_0)$.

The results are assembled in the following display:

Table 2.

	Neutral theory		Symmetric theory	
	1. cutoff rule	2. cutoff rule	1. cutoff rule	2. cutoff rule
r_0 (in 10^{-13} cm)	0.695	0.885	3.05	3.77
$f^2/\hbar c$	0.0800	0.0770	0.181	0.152
$(\overline{r'^2})^{\frac{1}{2}}$ (10^{-13} cm)	1.82	1.81	2.88	2.74
q (in 10^{-27} cm²)	+2.71	+2.62	−20.0	−17.9

In this the meson mass was assumed to be 177 electron masses and the characteristic length was, accordingly, $1/\kappa = 2.185 \cdot 10^{-13}$ cms. The quantity r' signifies the separation of the proton from the center of gravity of the deuteron in the ground state; the mean value $(\overline{r'^2})^{\frac{1}{2}}$ can, therefore, be regarded as about the radius of the deuteron. The quadrupole moment was calculated according to the assumption $q = 3\overline{z'^2} - \overline{r'^2}$; it states that the positional eigenfunction does not depend on r alone. This arises from the fact that, in consequence of the spin-orbital coupling, V_2, the ground state of the deuteron is a mixture of a dominant S-state with a D-state. Since only the total angular momentum and the total spin, but not the orbital momentum, are true quantum numbers, two possibilities are open: either there is no orbital momentum and a spin momentum $\hbar$, or the orbital momentum is $2\hbar$ and the spin $\hbar$ has the opposite direction, so that overall the empirical total momentum $\hbar$ is realized.

The two quantities r_0 and $f^2/\hbar c$ are so determined that the binding energies of the ground state and of the excited state are correctly reproduced. One sees that the results are, to a large extent, independent of the nature of the cutoff prescription; on the whole a much larger structure results from the symmetrical than from the neutral theory. Corresponding to its porous structure it is necessary to have a larger value of $f^2/\hbar c$ in the symmetrical theory in order to obtain a binding energy equal to the empirical value. One is considerably prejudiced against drawing quantitative conclusions from the symmetrical theory by the fact that the cut-off radius in it is greater than the mean distance of the proton from the center of gravity. That means that the two heavy particles often find themselves separated by distances for which the meson theory, because of its divergence difficulties, no longer applies.

The possibility for a quantitative control is afforded by the value of the quadrupole moment q. It is known, empirically, to be $2.75 \cdot 10^{-27}$ cm.^{2} It is seen that the neutral theory reproduces this value very well, whereas the symmetrical theory leads to an erroneous result, as regards both the sign and the order of magnitude.

In summary, it may, therefore, be stated that for a quantitative treatment of even the simplest problem of nuclear physics the meson theory is far from being the right language. The neutral theory is not able to explain the β-decay nor the actual appearance of charged mesons in cosmic radiation. The symmetrical theory breaks down completely in the quantitative treatment of deuterons. Both are beset by arbitrary cut-off rules which imply a much more serious encumbrance here than in the relativistic quantum mechanics. The great hope which was first placed in the meson theory has, therefore, not been fulfilled. But, after all that has been brought out in these two chapters, this is not very astonishing since we have apparently now gone beyond the limit of applicability of the existing schemes; processes with several particles, nonlinearity of equations, and similar things may create an entirely new situation for which our mathematical apparatus is in no way adapted.

12. THEORY OF EXPLOSION-LIKE SHOWERS

By W. HEISENBERG, Berlin-Dahlem

The effective cross-section for any kind of a collision process has almost always been calculated by means of a quantum mechanical perturbation theory known as the Born collision theory. Since the matrix of the interaction energy contains, in general, only elements for transitions in which one or at most two particles are created, it is necessary in general to extend the perturbation calculations to the nth (or, respectively, the nth$/2$) approximation if processes are to be accounted for in which n particles are created at a time. If the perturbation calculation converges reasonably, then the probability for the simultaneous emission of many particles becomes very small. This general consideration has led to the supposition that there can be practically no genuine multiple processes of this kind; and also, in the Yukawa Theory, Yukawa (Y 1 to 6), Bhabha (B 19, 20) and Heitler (H 5, 6) have calculated the effective cross-section for scattering, according to the Born method, and have assumed that the convergence of the perturbation method, which is always a problem because of the known divergences (self energy of a particle), could be established in a later and more complete form of the theory.

The more precise investigation of this question (Heisenberg) (H 3)), on the contrary, has led to the result that the Yukawa Theory already belongs to a group of theories in which the perturbation calculations are basically non-convergent when the colliding particle is above a certain energy. The Yukawa Theory is, therefore, one in which genuine explosive showers above this energy are to be expected. The reason for this property of the Yukawa theory will be given in the following discussion without detailed mathematical analysis.

There are two reasons for the occurrence of multiple processes in the Yukawa theory: first the close relationship of the Yukawa particle with the light-quantum, and second, the peculiarities of the energy of interaction between mesons and nuclear particles which are associated with the spin and charge of the meson.

The close formal relation between mesons and light-quanta which comes out of the Yukawa theory has as consequence that in the collision of two energetic nuclear particles several mesons can be created in the same way as an infinite number of light quanta are normally produced in the collision of two electrically charged particles. The latter fact was made understandable on the basis of the quantum theory in a paper by Bloch and Nord-sieck (B 27): When an energetic particle is suddenly deflected, according to the classical theory, at the moment of deflection the difference of the electromagnetic fields surrounding the particle before and after the deflection becomes in a certain sense detached and wanders into space as radiation. This radiation field at the moment of its creation is evidently a relatively small wave packet, and its Fourier expansion at that time gives a spectrum, the intensity of which approaches a constant value in the range of very low frequencies. This spectrum in the quantum mechanical interpretation represents the expectancy for the actual spectrum. The mean number dn of light quanta in the frequency interval $d\nu$ is, therefore, (cf., for example, the well-known formula for the x-ray spectrum)

$$dn \sim \text{const} \, \frac{d\nu}{h\nu}, \qquad (1)$$

and the integral over all frequencies leads to an infinite number of very low-energy light quanta.

In complete analogy to this, in the sudden deflection of a very energetic proton or of a neutron, the difference of the associated Yukawa fields before and after the deflection becomes detached and wanders into space as meson radiation. Again a spectrum is created with expectancy given approximately by (1). The total number of mesons now turns out to be finite since the meson possesses a finite rest mass; the integral over dn has a lower limit $h\nu = \mu c^2$. From this it follows that the mean number of mesons increases with the logarithm of the available collision energy, since the upper limit of (1) lies in the region where $h\nu$ is comparable with the primary energy E. Thus it follows:

$$n \sim \text{const} \cdot \log \frac{E}{\mu c^2}. \qquad (2)$$

The constant factor has a value of the order $e^2/\hbar c$ in the theory of light quanta, and in the Yukawa theory of the order $g^2/\hbar c$; its derivation will be omitted. The above-mentioned effect thus gives in principle the possibility of understanding the creation of several mesons in a single act, but only with extremely high energies of the colliding particle. This effect alone will scarcely suffice to explain the experiments.

The Yukawa theory differs from the theory of light quanta in a second essential feature: It contains terms in the interaction between the heavy particles and the Yukawa field which increase without limit with increasing energy of the particle considered. One can see this most simply by a dimensional analysis. Dimensionally, any physical quantity can be transformed to a power of a length by multiplication with suitable powers of $\hbar$ and c.

If in this way one measures all field quantities in units of $\hbar$ and c, then, in the Maxwellian theory, there remains only one dimensionless interaction constant $\left(\text{namely } \dfrac{e}{(\hbar c)^{\frac{1}{2}}}\right)$; the convergence of a perturbation calculation, therefore, depends upon the value of this constant alone. The Yukawa theory, on the contrary, because of the spin and charge of the meson, contains interaction terms with a constant of the dimensions of a length (and of the order of magnitude 10^{-13} cm.) This has the result that each perturbation calculation finally diverges if the wave length of the particle concerned is small with respect to this constant. The divergence of the perturbation procedure, moreover, has the significance of allowing for the possibility of exciting many mesons in a single act.

In detail this creation of explosive showers takes place in the following manner: Just as the excitation of electron-positron pairs in the radiation theory gives rise, in the Maxwellian equations, to nonlinear terms which lead to the scattering of light by light (Euler and Kochel (E 6)), so also in the Yukawa theory there are nonlinear terms, associated with proton-neutron pairs, which effect a scattering of mesons by mesons (Heisenberg (H 3)). These nonlinear terms are, in general, very small. However, in the very dense wave packets which are given off in the deflection of very energetic heavy particles they play an even greater part than the normal linear terms, if the energy is great enough. Thus the nonlinear terms produce a kind of turbulent mixing of the wave packet until it has expanded into such a large volume that the nonlinear terms lose their significance. In this process the Fourier spectrum of the wave packet undergoes a displacement toward the lower frequencies signifying the creation of many low energy mesons. A quantitative calculation of the meson spectrum within such an explosive shower is still impossible in the present state of the theory. One can make only the rather obvious statement that such a shower, in general, will contain many more low-energy than high-energy mesons and that the mean number of particles will increase with the available primary energy. On the other hand, the form of the meson spectrum will depend only slightly upon the primary energy.

The fundamental assumption of the Yukawa theory, namely, that the mesons of the cosmic radiation carry a spin of a whole number and that they are the producers of the nuclear forces, is not at the moment fully confirmed experimentally. Wigner, Critchfield, and Teller (W 8), for example, have proposed a theory of nuclear forces in which the forces are supplied by a pair of particles of spin 1/2, the question remaining open as to whether these particles are identical with the observed mesons. In such a theory the first of the above mentioned causes for the creation of genuine multiple processes drops out, but the second is still as valid as in the Yukawa theory.

In fact the possibility of explosion-like multiple processes was first studied on the basis of a theory of the same kind as that of Wigner, Critchfield, and Teller, namely, the Fermi β-decay theory (Heisenberg (H 1)).

Looking back over this situation in the theory it is gratifying that the experiments of recent years have pretty well established the existence of explosion-like showers (cf. Chapter 5, Klemm and Heisenberg). For the cross-section, calculated according to the conventional perturbation theory, one can expect agreement with the experiments only in the range of small energies when effects are involved depending on the Yukawa field. The purely electromagnetic effects of the meson, however, can probably be treated without these restrictions by the conventional theory. But it will be necessary to reckon with the possibility that the effective cross-section, thus calculated, for example, for the excitation of radiation by the collision of a meson, does not measure the probability for the emission of one light-quantum alone, but that it measures the probability for the emission of a light-quantum and for the simultaneous creation of some low-energy light-quanta and mesons (cf. the work of Bloch and Nordheim). One must also reckon with the possibility that, for example, the cascades which are set off by radiation excited by meson collisions may also contain a number of slow mesons (cf. Chapt. 5, v. Weizsacker). There are still no experiments bearing directly on this question.

NUCLEAR PARTICLES

13. NUCLEAR DISRUPTIONS AND HEAVY PARTICLES IN COSMIC RADIATION

By Erich Bagge, Berlin-Dahlem

1. Introduction: Statement of the Problem

In carefully examining photographic plates which had been exposed to cosmic radiation for a long time, Blau and Wambacher (B 25) in 1937 discovered the phenomenon of nuclear disruptions. These were recognized from the fact that within the gelatin layer several rows of developed silver grains produced by the nuclear fragments which flew off in the process of nuclear disruption radiated out from a common center (Fig. 1). In many of the observed tracks the range of the particles was so great that a confusion of this phenomenon with the so called "stars" from radioactive contamination could be excluded.

The proof that nuclear disruption is induced by cosmic rays was brought out by Stetter and Wambacher (S 19) when they were able to show by measurements at various locations that the frequency of this process increases very rapidly with elevation above sea level.

Independently of these phenomena, the separate protons and neutrons appearing in the cosmic radiation have been the subject of several investigations (Widhalm (W 7), Schopper (S 11, 12), Rumbaugh and Locher (R 12), Fünfer (F 5, 6), Korff (K 6), Montgomery and Montgomery (M 6)). Moreover, the frequency of occurrence of these particles shows a dependence on altitude similar to that established for the nuclear disruptions, and it is natural to suppose that the two groups of phenomena are related.

In fact, it was also shown that in the lower atmosphere the proton and neutron intensities follow exactly the frequency of nuclear disruptions. The question of the identity of the radiation which liberates the heavy nuclear particles is, therefore, really the same as that of finding the source of the disruptive processes; all available evidence favors the view that the latter are excited by energetic light-quanta or electrons of the soft component of the cosmic radiation. The heavy particles and the nuclear disruptions are thus given a definite place in the overall picture of cosmic radiation.

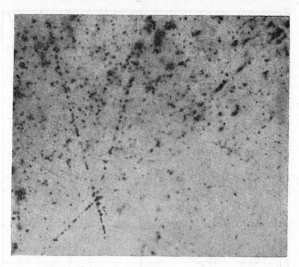

Figure 1. Example of a nuclear disruption in the photographic emulsion.

2. Frequencies of Nuclear Disruptions and of Heavy Particles at Various Elevations above Sea Level

The frequencies of nuclear disruptions at various elevations above sea level as determined by Stetter and Wambacher are shown in Fig. 2. Likewise, the data of Widhalm (W 7) are shown for the proton intensities, and the curve (I) gives the variation of the electron-photon intensity to be expected theoretically from the cascade theory. From this figure it is seen that the values for the frequencies of the nuclear disruptions show the same rapid increase with elevation as those for the single proton tracks. Moreover, both sets of data conform approximately to the theoretical curve for the intensity rise of the cascade electrons.

A certain difference is indicated between the rise in frequency of protons and that of nuclear disruptions: Whereas the ratio of the extreme values of the intensity of the protons is 64:1, the corresponding ratio for the nuclear disruptions has a value between 30 and 60:1. We note this fact here and will come back to it later (see bottom of p. 140).

The results of measurements of the neutron intensities at various elevations are shown in Fig. 3. Here also a comparison with the curve taken from Fig. 2 for the cascade electrons shows a frequency increase of the same order of magnitude as that of the observed single proton tracks. Likewise, the measurements of neutron frequencies by Korff, as well as the first measurements by Fünfer, are given and these fit the curve very well.

Accordingly, between the groups of phenomena here considered there

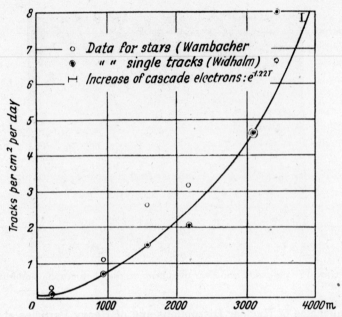

Figure 2. Frequency distribution of stars and single proton tracks as function of the elevation in the atmosphere.

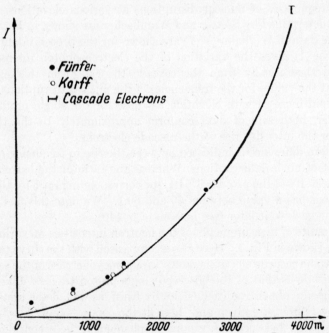

Figure 3. Frequency distribution of neutrons as a function of elevation in the atmosphere.

exists a far reaching parallelism in regard to their variation with elevation. It immediately appears that if one assumes that the nuclear disruptions are the real source from which the single tracks of heavy particles originate, and if it can be further shown that the effect of a single particle extends only over a range within which the intensity does not alter radically, then the similarity of the variations of frequency with elevation are explained in a most simple manner. The single tracks of the protons and neutrons can thus be considered simply as products of the nuclear disruptions.

According to both theory and experiment, something like the following picture can be formed of the nuclear process itself (B 1a): At first, possibly through the collision of a photon, one or more heavy particles in the nucleus are set into rapid motion. These energetic neutrons or protons in their passage through the nucleus collide with other heavy particles and impart more or less energy to these. These secondary particles can either leave the nucleus immediately or they can form tertiary particles until finally the greater part of the energy of the primary particle is distributed throughout the nucleus as thermal motion. Thus, the original collision process results in a nuclear evaporation in the sense of the Bohr theory of nuclear processes. The whole process also takes place in the same way if a very energetic proton or neutron strikes the atomic nucleus from outside. In general, it should be possible to divide the particles ejected from the nucleus into two groups: those thrown out of the nucleus directly as secondary particles and those released by chance through evaporation.

Corresponding to these ideas it is possible to represent the empirical spectrum (averaged over all "stars") of the ejected protons in the form

$$f(E)dE = \left(\frac{a}{\epsilon}\, e^{-E/\epsilon} + \frac{b}{\eta}\, e^{-E/\eta}\right)dE$$

with $a = 3.18$, $b = 1.60$, $\epsilon = 2.72$ MeV, $\eta = 17$ MeV. The second part of this spectrum is to be ascribed to the directly emitted protons and the first to the evaporated protons. The nuclear temperature in this process would then be of the order of magnitude of a few MeV. However, the partition of the spectrum into two exponential functions will not exactly correspond to the partition of the particles into the two groups; also one must consider that the temperature of the nucleus is gradually reduced during the evaporation.—Occasionally the view has been expressed that all Blau-Wambacher "stars" can be conceived simply as nuclear evaporation. Such an hypothesis, however, according to the empirical spectrum of the protons would lead to temperatures of 10-15 MeV and to total excitation energies which are far too high. Since one can evaluate the total energy of a disruption process, it must be concluded, by reversing the argument, that from the relative number of high energy protons it cannot be treated as a pure evaporation process. One can most probably describe what happens in the following manner: The heavy particle which penetrates the nucleus produces at the point of entry a very strong local heating and, in consequence, sends out relatively high-energy nuclear ingredients. Finally the heat dissipates itself gradually throughout the nucleus. This assumption, however, is only another formulation of the distribution of the emitted particles into two groups distinguished by their times of emission, as outlined above.

3. Nature and Energy of the Emitted Radiation

Next, a more precise treatment will be made of the question of the nature of the radiation which sets off the nuclear processes. As the most important indication of the answer to this question, one may consider the facts established by the data represented in Figs. 2 and 3, i.e., that the increase of

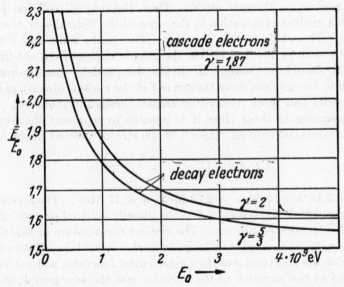

Figure 4. The mean energy of cascade electrons and the decay electrons as function of the lower limit E_0, above which nuclear disruptions can be released.

intensity with elevation of cascade electrons and photons, which is well established both experimentally and theoretically, is in close agreement with the rise in the number of disruption stars.

The analogous observation regarding the cascade electrons and the large Hoffman bursts led Euler (E 3) to assume that the bursts are excited by the energetic cascade particles. On the basis of their completely similar behavior the release of nuclear disruptions will also be regarded as an effect of the soft component of the cosmic radiation, but it must also be admitted that the energetic electrons resulting from decay of mesons can be effective in the process.

However, one encounters here a difficulty with this interpretation. For, whereas experimentally the mean energy of 89 MeV released by all nuclear disruptions at 200 m. elevation increases to 144 MeV at 3450 m., the mean energy of the cascade electrons remains constant over the same elevation interval, and that of the decay electrons falls off slightly as long as one takes into account that portion of the energy spectrum beyond about 5.10^8eV. If the lower limit is pushed to still smaller energies, this characteristic becomes even more marked.

The situation is somewhat different if one takes the average for the interval beyond a higher energy. This may be seen from Fig. 4. For conditions at sea level it shows the mean energy of the spectrum of the cascade electrons:

$$F_k = \text{const} \, \frac{e^{-1.22T}}{E^\gamma} \qquad (\gamma = 1.87; \, T \text{ in m water}) \qquad (1)$$

and the mean energy of the decay electrons:

$$F_z = \text{const} \, \frac{1}{E(E + aT)^\gamma} \qquad (a = 2 \cdot 10^8 \text{eV/m water}), \qquad (2)$$

as a function of the lower limit E_0 of the spectrum concerned, beyond which the mean is figured. It turns out that in the range $E > 10^9$ the mean energy of the decay electrons, $\overline{E}_z \approx 1.6E_0$, lies significantly below that of the cascade electrons $\overline{E}_k \approx 2.15 \, E_0$. On the other hand, it is recognized that very few low-energy cascade electrons are present at sea level and the decay electrons predominate, whereas, on the contrary, because of their exponential rise the cascade electrons represent the dominant portion at greater elevations. One, therefore, needs only to assume that, in actuality, the energetic part of the soft component $E > 5.10^9$eV is responsible for the release of the nuclear disruptions in order to understand the increase with elevation of the mean energy liberated by this process. For in this case one can realize a transition in going to greater elevations from an $\overline{E} \approx 1.6 \, E_0$ of the decay electrons to an $\overline{E} \approx 2.15 \, E_0$ of the cascade electrons. Unfortunately, the absolute values of the individual spectra are not well enough known at the moment, to enable one to follow this transition theoretically in detail.

In any case, however, one will conclude that the mean energy of the primary photons or electrons is at least an order of magnitude, and perhaps considerably more than this, greater than the energy liberated by the process as deduced from the energies of the emitted protons. This corresponds entirely with the observations on nuclear disruptions in the Wilson chamber (for example those of Fussell (F 7)). A compilation of the literature on Wilson chamber photographs of nuclear disruptions is given in a paper by Wambacher (W 1), in which it has been established that, in addition to the heavy particles, there are also frequent light-weight particles or electrons, and in a few cases some mesons were found which were most probably excited by a collision process.

4. The Single Proton Tracks as Products of Nuclear Disruptions

The question may now be raised as to how far it is possible to attribute the observed single proton tracks to the nuclear disruptions. In this, one must calculate the number of protons which strike a unit surface per day from all of the nuclear disruptions in the surrounding space.

In order to treat this question it is necessary to know the number of all nuclear disruptions in one cc. per day. From this knowledge, together with the energy spectrum of the disintegration protons determined by Wambacher, and by taking into account the energy losses of the protons by ionization in the air, one gets, immediately, the expected energy spectrum of the single tracks.

In this, however, one encounters two difficulties which can be only partially resolved.

In the first place, the frequency of the nuclear disruptions is known only for the gelatin films of photographic plates, whereas one needs to have it for air. It is, therefore, necessary to make a calculation as to what happens in air from what is observed to happen in the photographic emulsion. Such an evaluation can, naturally, be only approximately correct because of the different chemical constitutions of the two substances.

Moreover, there is the further difficulty that in all of the measurements made so far of the frequency of nuclear disruptions, no single and only a part of the double processes in which only one or two protons leave the nucleus have been counted. This results from the difficulty in the measuring procedure, i.e., that such processes fundamentally cannot be distinguished from recoil protons of fast neutrons or from sharply bent single tracks.

To evaluate these single and double disruptions one is, therefore, led to make certain extrapolations. These do not seem unplausible, but they are justified only if they succeed, with the same numerical values, in bringing both the frequency of the single proton tracks and that of the fast neutrons into approximate agreement with the results of the measurements, in spite of the fact that the frequencies of occurrence of the two kinds of particles differ from one another by about two orders of magnitude (B 16).

a) **Determination of the Energy Spectrum of the Single Proton Tracks** In the calculation of the energy spectrum of the single proton tracks one proceeds as follows: If n is the number of nuclear disruptions per cc. per day and $f(E_0)dE_0$ is the average energy spectrum of the protons emitted per process, then a number of particles

$$nf(E_0)\ dE_0\ d\tau\ \frac{\cos\theta}{4\pi r^2} \tag{3}$$

with energy between E_0 and $E_0 + dE_0$ would leave volume element $d\tau$ and strike a unit surface at the origin (cf. Fig. 5).

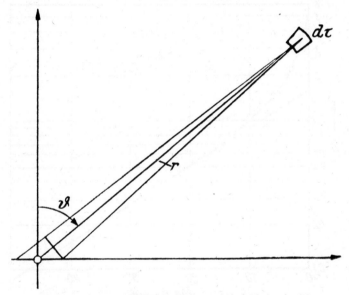

Figure 5. The significance of r, θ, and $d\tau$ in formula (3).

Along their path from $d\tau$ to 0 the particles will have lost energy by ionization in a known amount. The energy-range relation is represented by the formula: $R = \Phi(E_0)$. The energy E of the protons when they strike the origin is determined by the equation:

$$R - r = \Phi(E_0) - r = \Phi(E). \tag{4}$$

One, therefore, has a relation between the three quantities E_0, E, and r and can thereby express E_0 by E and r. By integrating the formula (3) over the upper half-space, a function $F(E)dE$ is obtained which describes the energy spectrum of all of the protons coming from this region and originating in nuclear disruptions.

For $f(E_0)dE_0$ one takes the spectrum derived by Wambacher which, as already mentioned, is represented in good approximation by the function

$$f(E_0) \, dE_0 = \left(\frac{a}{\epsilon} e^{-E_0/\epsilon} + \frac{b}{\eta} e^{-E_0/\eta} \right) dE_0, \qquad (5)$$

with $a = 3.18$, $b = 1.60$, $\epsilon = 2.72$ MeV and $\eta = 17$ MeV.

Wambacher's measurements and the function (5) are represented in Fig. 6. As one sees, in the range between 0 and 50 MeV, they are in very good agreement.

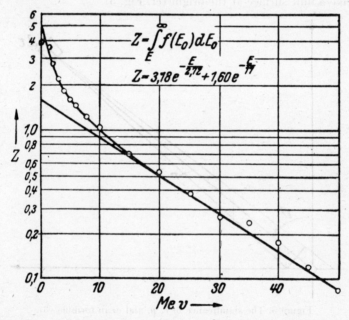

Figure 6. Frequency distribution of disruption protons as function of the energy.

If the calculation is carried through with this distribution function (B 1), the desired function $F(E)dE$ is obtained. The integration over the latter results in a relation between the total frequency N_p of protons per cm.² per day and the frequency n of the nuclear processes per cc. per day. One obtains

$$\frac{N_p}{n} = 230 \text{ cm.} \qquad (6)$$

This ratio will be compared with the corresponding numerical values taken from the measurements.

b) **Comparison of the Total Frequencies.**   The distribution function $F(E)dE$ resulting from the preceding calculation is shown in Fig. 7.   The

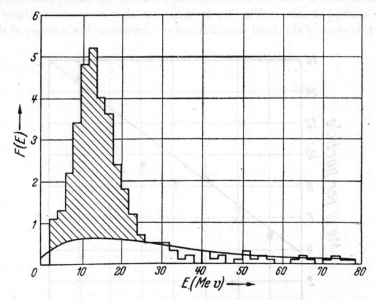

Figure 7. Energy distribution of single proton tracks. Step curve: Measurements of WIDHALM. Smooth curve: Theoretical curve $F(E)dE$.

same figure also contains the corresponding data on proton frequencies taken from the measurements by Widhalm.   The function $F(E)dE$ is here so normalized that it agrees with the measured values at about 25 MeV.   As the figure shows, it represents the experimental results very well for all higher energies.   On the contrary, the curves deviate from one another completely at the lower energies.   This can be attributed principally to the fact that in Wambacher's measurements he failed to include the single and double disruptions.   This assumption immediately explains the above mentioned shape of $F(E)dE$.

The mean energy of the nuclear fragments from the single and double processes is of the order of magnitude 4 to 5 MeV.   This is taken directly from Fig. 8, which gives the measured mean value of the particle energies for the three, four, etc. "stars" as a function of the number of emitted protons.   The measured points fall approximately along a straight line, which begins with a 15 MeV mean energy for the eight particle "stars" and then falls off for smaller proton numbers.   The extrapolation to the particle number *one* leads to a mean value of about 4 MeV. The existence of single and double disruptions will, therefore, be able to influence the shape of $F(E)dE$ only in the small energy range up to about 20 MeV.

One can now evaluate the approximate number of the single and double disruptions which were not included, if he measures the ratio of the shaded to the unshaded area in Fig. 7. It turns out that about three times as many processes of this kind were left out of account as the number of dis-

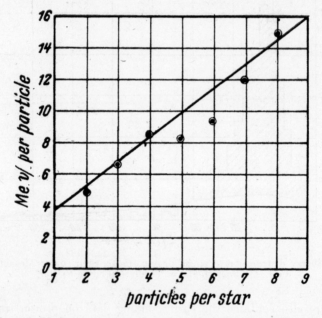

Figure 8. Mean energy per particle for stars of fixed particle number.

ruptions found with the higher number of particles. The total frequency of the nuclear processes should, therefore, be four times as great as that given by Wambacher's data.

This agrees very well with the findings on the frequency distribution of the various "stars", as represented in Fig. 9. The total frequency of all "stars" with particle number ν exceeding that given as abscissa, falls in excellent fashion on a straight line for $\nu = 3$ to 8. If one tries to extend this line to small particle numbers, he obtains for $\nu = 1$ a frequency (≈ 50) which is four or five times the value measured for $\nu = 2$ (11), in satisfactory agreement with above result. With regard to such an extrapolatory determination of the frequency of these processes, one can naturally hold certain misgivings. However, it is to be noted that this procedure, on account of the relationships brought out in Fig. 8, may be considered as good as an extrapolation made with the help of the particle number or as a determination using the mean proton energies.

It is still to be shown that by taking into account the missing single and double processes the observed absolute frequencies of single proton tracks can be attributed to the nuclear disruptions.

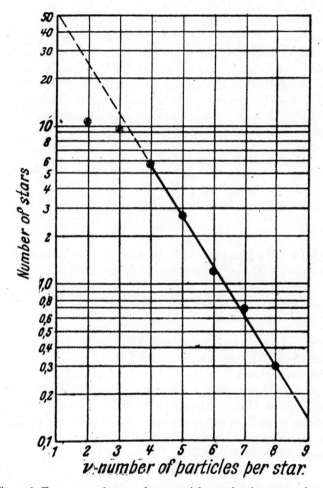

Figure 9. Frequency of stars whose particle number is greater than ν.

According to Stetter and Wambacher, 0.03 nuclear processes take place per cm.² per day in a 100μ thick film of the photographic plate at an elevation of 3450 m. In the film about 4/5 of the nuclei are of the type (O, C, N) and about 1/5 Ag and Br. Their total number is, therefore, essentially determined by the frequency of the first kind in the gelatin, whose density is nearly 1. One can then expect

$$n \approx \frac{3 \cdot 1.3}{1000} \approx 4 \cdot 10^{-3}$$

"stars" per cc. per day in air.

At the same elevation there are 8.02 protons per cm.^{2} per day according to Widhalm and 1.44 protons per cm.^{2} per day according to Schopper (S 11). In these values, moreover, the protons of the single and double processes are included. In order to have a comparable ratio only a quarter of these should be attributed to disruptions involving more than two particles, according to the considerations at the beginning of this section; thus one obtains from Widhalm $N_p = 2$ protons per cm.^{2} per day, and from Schopper $N_p = 0.36$ protons per cm.^{2} per day. From this one gets

$$\left(\frac{N_p}{n}\right)_{exp} \cong \begin{cases} \dfrac{2}{4 \cdot 10^{-3}} = 500 \text{ cm. (Widhalm),} \\[2em] \dfrac{0.36}{4 \cdot 10^{-3}} = 90 \text{ cm. (Schopper).} \end{cases} \tag{7}$$

This result is to be compared with the ratio (6) which was already derived for the processes with more than two particles:

$$\left(\frac{N_p}{n}\right)_{theor} = 230 \text{ cm.}$$

The result to be expected theoretically thus lies between the experimental determinations of Widhalm and Schopper.

It is, therefore, shown that the frequency of the single proton tracks can be attributed to the nuclear disruptions. To explain the appearance of such particles in the lower atmosphere it is not necessary to suppose that these particles come from external space. More probably their appearance should be regarded as a necessary consequence of the nuclear disintegrations released by the soft component of cosmic radiation.

In this connection it is to be expected that the proton intensity will increase with elevation somewhat faster than the frequency of nuclear disruptions since it is already known that the mean energy of the disintegration particles increases slowly with elevation and for this reason at the same time the mean range of the protons becomes larger. An effect in this direction seems to be indicated by a comparison of the measurements of Widhalm and Wambacher.

5. The Fast Neutrons as Products of Nuclear Disruptions

In the nuclear disruptions neutrons as well as protons are emitted. The former, however, cannot be observed immediately in the photographic emulsion, but if charged particles leave the nucleus in such collision-processes, naturally the uncharged neutrons will also be knocked out. As regards the number of emitted neutrons one will not be far off in the assumption that about as many particles of one kind as of the other leave the nucleus. This assumption will form the basis for the following considerations; in complete analogy with the procedure for the protons, it will be shown that the frequency of *fast* neutrons obtained from a simple estimate agrees approximately with that found from the experiments.

This determination should pertain only to the fast neutrons. The behavior of the slow neutrons will be discussed in a chapter by Flügge. Here we will consider the fast neutrons that can be detected, according to the method used by Schopper, by the recoil protons from a thin layer of parafin.

One can also simply assume, as has been extensively discussed by Bethe, Korff and Placzek (B 17), that the fast neutrons disappear when they strike an atomic nucleus, for example N_7^{14}. In many cases they will leave the nucleus again with reduced energy, but they will then be within the range of velocity where they can no longer be detected photographically by their recoil protons from the parafin layer.

Let their mean free path to the first nuclear encounter be λ. Then in complete analogy with the derivation in the case of the protons, one obtains for the number of particles which originate in the volume element $d\tau$ at distance r and strike a unit surface

$$n\nu \, d\tau \, \frac{\cos \theta}{4\pi r^2} \, e^{-r/\lambda}. \tag{8}$$

Here ν is the mean number of neutrons emitted in one process.

By integrating (8) over r and θ in the upper half-space one gets, N_n, the total number of incident neutrons.

$$\frac{N_n}{n} = \frac{\lambda\nu}{4}. \tag{9}$$

Wambacher's table gives the value 3.88 for the mean number of protons per star. Thus we take for the neutrons

$$\nu = 4 \text{ neutrons per star.}$$

The free path λ, with a collision cross section of $\sigma = 10^{-24}$ cm.^{2}, turns out to be 360 m. normal air.

Thus,

$$\frac{N_n}{n} = \tfrac{1}{4} \cdot 3.6 \cdot 10^4 \cdot 4 = 3.6 \cdot 10^4 \text{ cm.} \tag{10}$$

On the other hand, one can calculate the above relation directly from N_n and n if one takes N_n from the measurements of Schopper and bases n on the discussion of page 140.

At 3450 m. elevation behind 1 mm. parafin Schopper finds 5.3 recoil protons per cm.^{2} per day. Neglecting the very slight absorption in the parafin itself, the number ΔZ of recoil protons turns out to be

$$\Delta Z = N_n \cdot \sigma \cdot n_H \cdot \Delta x \tag{11}$$

and hence

$$N_n = \frac{\Delta Z}{\sigma n_H \Delta x} \tag{12}$$

(n_H = number of protons per cc. in parafin = $9 \cdot 10^{22}$,
Δx = thickness of the layer = 0.1 cm., $\sigma = 10^{-24}$ cm.^{2})

$$N_n = \frac{5.3}{9 \cdot 10^{22} \cdot 0.1 \cdot 10^{-24}} \cong 600 \text{ per cm}^2 \text{ per day} \tag{13}$$

If we again take into account the fact that in the derivation of this number all single and double disruptions were counted, whereas, in the determination of $n = 4.10^{-3}$ per cc. per day on page 140, only the processes with the higher particle numbers were counted, then N_m must be replaced by $N_m/4$ in order to have comparable relationships.

In this way one gets

$$\frac{N_n}{n} = \frac{600}{4 \cdot 4 \cdot 10^{-3}} \cong 4 \cdot 10^4 \text{ cm.} \tag{14}$$

The two numerical values for the ratio (N_n/n) obtained on the one hand from theoretical considerations (10), and on the other hand from experimental determination (14), therefore, are in practical agreement. Although, because of the uncertainty inherent in the effective cross-section, it is partly accidental that the two numerical values agree so perfectly, there can be scarcely any doubt that the two numbers are of the same order of magnitude. More than this is not to be expected from the present state of the experimental determinations.

Nevertheless, it can now be established that such frequencies of fast neutrons as are actually observed experimentally are to be expected as products of the nuclear disruptions alone. The frequencies of the nuclear processes used in this calculation are the same as those upon which the considerations of the proton intensities were based.

It is thus shown that the frequencies of the protons, as well as those of the neutrons in the lower atmosphere, can be attributed to the nuclear disruptions. The hypothesis that such particles penetrate into this region from external space is, accordingly, superfluous.

The state of the experimental investigations in the upper regions of the atmosphere do not allow the relationships there to be reviewed at the moment. Only after one succeeds in obtaining suitable numerical data on the frequencies of the various groups of phenomena can it be proved to what extent the heavy particles in this part of the atmosphere are to be considered as products of nuclear disruptions.

14. ON THE EXCITATION OF NEUTRONS BY COSMIC RAYS AND THEIR DISTRIBUTION IN THE ATMOSPHERE

By S. Flügge, Berlin

1. Experimental Facts

The first observations of neutrons in the atmosphere were made by Fünfer 1937 (F 5). He used a proportional counter of large volume (2800 cc.), of which the inner surface was lined with a boron layer. When this chamber was surrounded on all sides by a thick borax shield (10 Kg.), the number of counts registered fell from (10.85 ± 0.23) per min. to (9.5 ± 0.2) per min. at the Giessen Institute. The difference of 1.35 ± 0.3 counts per min. had to be ascribed to slow neutrons. These first observations gave impetus to a systematic investigation of the effect. First, layers of hydrogenous substances (water, parafin, wood) were placed around to slow the fast neutrons down a little and thus to make them effective for measurement in the boron chamber. Whereas within the Giessen Laboratory, where the neutrons were already slowed down by passage through the concrete roof, no influence of such layers appeared, the measurements in free air gave about a two fold increase:

> Without parafin 0.65 ± 0.1 neutron/min.
> With 1 cm. parafin 1.3 ± 0.12 neutron/min.
> With 4 cm. parafin 1.25 ± 0.12 neutron/min.
> With up to 45 cms. H_2O the same.

With wood also the same increase of the effect could be obtained up to saturation at about 1.3 per min. On the contrary, no such augmentation was obtained with layers of lead, a fact which again is typical of the behavior of neutrons.

Measurements were then undertaken by Fünfer in 1938 (F 6) at various elevations with the chamber surrounded on all sides by a 2 cm. thick wooden box. Again the differences were measured with and without borax. The following counts were obtained:

Table 1.

Place	Altitude m.	Atmospheric pressure atm.	Neutrons per min.	$N_0 e^{-\mu p}$ $\mu = 6.93$
Giessen	160	0.99	1.27 ± 0.09	1.27
Hoherodskopf . . .	780	0.91	2.1 ± 0.36	2.18
Feldberg in	1280	0.85	3.2 ± 0.3	3.19
Schwarzwald . . .	1500	0.82	4.2 ± 0.2	4.12
Zugspitze	2650	0.71	9.8 ± 0.25	8.65

If one tries to represent the experimental counts by a law of the form $N = N_0 e^{-\mu p}$ where p is the pressure in atmospheres, then with $\mu = 6.93$ one obtains the last column of the table, which is in quite good agreement with the measurements.

At about the same time Schopper began investigations to detect neutrons in the cosmic radiation. By a procedure similar to that of Blau and Wambacher (B 25), photographic plates were exposed at different elevations and the tracks of heavy particles formed in the emulsion were counted. In this work two different procedures could be used for separate observation of fast and slow neutrons. In order to detect fast neutrons the plates were placed first behind 1 mm. of lead and again behind 1 mm. of parafin. Whereas the number of tracks behind the lead could be regarded as a measure of the number of protons present, the considerably increased number of proton tracks behind the parafin layer indicated that protons were being ejected from the parafin by primary heavy particles. These particles were thought to be fast neutrons. The following counts were obtained.

Table 2.

Place	Altitude m	Atmospheric pressure atm	Protons per cm² per hour with		$N_0 e^{-\mu p}$ $\mu = 6.93$
			1 mm parafin	1 mm lead	
Stuttgart . . .	200	0.98	0.07	?	0.02
Jugfraujoch . .	3400	0.65	0.28	0.06	0.22
Stratosphere . .	18000	0.09	5.1	?	10.2

In the last column numbers have again been chosen to correspond to the exponential absorption which Fünfer found in the lower third of the atmosphere. Since the null effect with lead was measured at but one point, these numbers can be compared only very roughly with the experimental values. Nevertheless, it can be definitely concluded that Schopper's stratosphere value is smaller than it should be according to the exponential extrapolation.

The measurements of the slow neutrons were made in the following manner by Schopper: He used a photographic emulsion containing boron, in which α-particles of 1.89 MeV energy were given off by the slow neutrons in the reaction $^{10}B(n,\alpha)^7Li$, and their tracks were observed in the emulsion. At one time a boron absorber was laid over the plate to absorb the slow neutrons. Again, he worked without the boron absorber, and a strong increase in the α-tracks took place. Observations were made at two places: In Stuttgart 0.15 α-particles per cm.² per hour were found, and on the Jungfraujoch the number was 0.25. This increase is very much less than was to be expected, according to Fünfer's absorption coefficient.

Korff (K 6) has also carried out investigations of the neutron intensity up to very great heights. The measurements were made with counter tubes 20 cm. long and 2 cm. diameter, and filled with BF_3 gas at 0.1 atm. pressure. In this way the total number of all slow neutrons was counted. The measurements extend to pressures of about 1/20 atm. and throughout show the same rate of increase which can be represented by an exponential function with $\mu = 7$ per atm.

The absolute number of neutrons can also be deduced from Korff's measurements. However, in this there is involved a series of poorly known quantities, especially the excitation of recoil nuclei in the boron chamber which are released by primary particles other than the neutrons. Hence, all absolute values are uncertain by at least a factor of two in one or the other direction. From Korff's measurements, which he, Bethe, and Placzek have discussed extensively, a production of 0.05 neutrons per gram per sec. takes place in the region of the atmosphere where the pressure is 0.1 atm. That agrees well with the value obtained from an airplane flight which v. Halban, Kowarski and Magat supervised in Paris up to 9500 m. elevation (0.3 atm.). In these measurements the neutrons were slowed down in a solution of C_2H_5Br; the active bromine created could then be separated out by a Szilard-Chalmers process, and in this manner considerable activity was attained. The discussion of these investigations by Bethe, Korff and Placzek led to a neutron production of 0.01 neutrons per g. per sec., which, at the lower elevations, agreed well with the value of Korff. If this production is integrated over the whole atmosphere with the absorption coefficient $\mu = 7$,[1] one obtains a neutron production amounting in all to about 15 neutrons per cm.[2] per sec. in the entire atmosphere.

2. Nuclear Physics Background

To understand the observed neutron distribution in the atmosphere it is necessary to know the interaction between neutrons and the air atoms. The experimental material on this question is not so plentiful as might be desired, yet it is sufficient to provide a preliminary survey. This is to be presented here, following closely the work of Bethe, Korff and Placzek.

We know only incompletely what happens when neutrons of more than 30 MeV encounter nitrogen or oxygen nuclei (cf. the previous chapter). If, on the other hand, their energy is smaller, we can more confidently use the Bohr model of the atomic nucleus (sandsack model). According to this, the effective cross-section for inelastic scattering of the neutrons will be of the order of the geometric nuclear cross-section ($\sim 10^{-24}$ cm.[2]) and

---

[1]This corresponds to an effective cross-section of 2×10^{-25} cm^2.

in such scatterings the neutrons on the average are slowed down to a few MeV.   Below 6 MeV in oxygen and 4 MeV in nitrogen no more inelastic collisions can take place since the lowest excitation levels of these nuclei are at these energies.

Regarding the elastic scattering which effects further stoppage of the neutrons a few experimental values are known.   Thus it is known that the scattering cross-section of ^{14}N as well as of ^{16}O varies but little in the range from 3 MeV to 0.15 MeV, whereas it increases to considerably greater values in the range of thermal neutron energies (1/40 eV).

Table 3.

Process	Effective cross section in 10^{-24} cm² for neutron energies of			Threshold energy MeV
	3 MeV	0.15 MeV	1/40 eV (thermal)	
Elastic scattering on ^{14}N . .	1.4	1.6	10.7	—
Elastic scattering on ^{16}O . .	1.2	1.8	4.2	—
^{14}N (n, p) ^{14}C	0.04	?	1.3	—
^{14}N (n, α) ^{11}B	0.16	—	—	0.30
^{16}O (n, p) ^{16}N	—	—	—	5.6
^{16}O (n, α) ^{13}C	~0.01	—	—	2.6

The effective cross-section for the capture process is certainly very small. Something is known about the capture reaction of protons ^{14}N(p,γ) ^{15}O and ^{16}O(p,γ) ^{17}F, both of which take place with proton energies of 4 MeV and an effective cross-section of only $0.15 \cdot 10^{-28}$ cm.² (Curran and Strothers (C 10)).   Since the Gamow factor at these energies for such light nuclei cannot be much smaller than 1, one should expect that the two capture processes for neutrons (n,γ) would not exceed in order of magnitude 10^{-28} cm.²

The survey shows that the only nuclear reaction which has to be taken into account in addition to the elastic collisions is the (n,p) process in nitrogen, since the other three reactions given in the table are endothermic and, in general, do not take place for small neutron energies.   Unfortunately, the variation with energy of the cross-section for the (n,p) reaction in ^{14}N is not well known.   This is the more regrettable since resonances which are still unknown surely determine the two measured values of the cross-section.   If one were to assume a smooth variation of the reaction curve, then the cross-section should be inversely proportional to the velocity of the neutrons and, besides, proportional to a Gamow factor for the emission of the proton.   According to this, one would expect a cross-section of around $13 \cdot 10^{-24}$ cm.² for thermal neutrons, whereas actually it only amounts to a tenth of this value.

As a plausible explanation for this one can assume that the value for 3

MeV neutron energies is abnormally high because of a resonance lying in this range. Since with such light-weight nuclei the breadth of a resonance line amounts to about 10 keV, one may well assume that the effective cross-section for small energies follows the $1/v$ law out to about 10 keV; the Gamow factor in this range can be regarded as practically constant.

As an approximation in what follows we therefore use the model proposed by Bethe and his coworkers; neutrons which are originally faster than about 6 MeV are slowed down by inelastic scattering almost immediately to an energy of a few MeV. Then practically all of the scattering is elastic, a fact which effects a further slowing down. Finally, below 10 keV the (n,p) cross-section in nitrogen gradually begins to play a part, for which we write

$$\sigma_{abs} = \frac{0.16}{(E)^{\frac{1}{2}}} \cdot 10^{-24} \text{ cm}^2,$$

if E is the neutron energy in electron volts. The appearance of this reaction leads finally to an absorption of the slow neutrons. The experimental data for the effective cross-section for elastic scattering show that in the range of fast neutrons apparently only small variations are present. Hence, the scattering cross-section of an air atom will be put equal to a constant average value of $1.35 \cdot 10^{-24}$ cm.^{2} above an energy E_s, which certainly cannot be larger than 0.15 MeV. Under this energy an increase in the cross-section determined by resonance comes in as the large value for thermal neutrons shows. Since in elastic scattering the $1/v$ law is not involved, one may well regard the scattering cross-section as a constant up to at least 10 keV, amounting to $9.4 \cdot 10^{-24}$ cm.^{2} for the average air atom. Thus the following simple model may be used.

$$\sigma_{\text{Scat.}} = \begin{cases} 1.35 \cdot 10^{-24} \text{ cm.}^2 \text{ for } E > E_s \\ 9.4 \cdot 10^{-24} \text{ cm.}^2 \text{ for } E < E_s \end{cases}$$

and $10 \text{ keV} < E_s < 150 \text{ keV}.$

Naturally the assumption of the existence of a transition point of this kind is a very rough approximation. It would be especially desirable to study somewhat more thoroughly the rôle of the chemical bond of scattering atoms in the N_2 and O_2 molecules.

Here we need the free path λ in the atmosphere corresponding to the scattering cross-section in addition to the cross-section itself. Since this depends on the air pressure p we introduce instead of it the quantity

$$l = \frac{\lambda}{h}p \tag{1}$$

which is independent of the pressure, and in which $h \sim 8$ km. signifies the height of the homogeneous atmosphere. The quantity l then has the dimensions of a pressure; numerically

$$l = \begin{cases} 18 \cdot 10^{-3} \text{ atm. for } E > E_s \\ \\ 2.6 \cdot 10^{-3} \text{ atm. for } E < E_s. \end{cases} \quad (2)$$

3. Consequences of the Diffusion Theory

a) The neutrons which we observe in the atmosphere cannot be of cosmic origin, but must have been excited as secondaries in the passage of some other kind of cosmic ray particle through the atmosphere. This conclusion cannot be established at the present time immediately from observations; however, it follows from the β-instability of the neutron, which possesses a greater mass than a neutral hydrogen atom and hence should go over into this form by β-decay. The half-life can be obtained from the Sargent diagram, which shows it to be of the order of one hour. It should be expressly noted that the β-decay of the neutron has not yet been observed experimentally since the interaction of neutrons with the atomic nuclei of the experimental apparatus is always so strong that the neutrons vanish long before they reach such an age.

b) It will, therefore, be assumed that a source of definite but unknown strength for neutrons must be ascribed to the atmosphere. We will consider the fate of the neutrons originating in the atmosphere during a short time interval at $t = 0$. Their density at the moment of their formation is naturally proportional to the strength of the source; let it be $\rho_0(p)$, in which the air pressure p is introduced as a suitable variable in place of the elevation z.

The neutrons now undergo a stopping process in which their velocity drops from an initial value v_0 (energy E_0). The momentary velocity v (energy E) of a neutron is, therefore, on the average a function of the number ν of elastic collisions which it has made since the time of its formation, as well as of the initial velocity v_0, which in this paragraph is assumed the same for all neutrons. It will prove to be expedient to introduce this collision number into the calculations as the independent variable in place of the time; the two are related by the equation

$$\frac{d\nu}{dt} = \frac{v(\nu)}{\lambda},$$

or, since, according to equation (1), $\lambda = h \cdot l(\nu)/p$,

$$dt = d\nu \cdot \frac{h}{p} \frac{l(\nu)}{v(\nu)}. \quad (3)$$

Since this condition has only a statistical meaning, its introduction implies an approximation, which, however, should give rise to no appreciable error in the solution of our problem.

Besides the stopping process the neutrons experience a change of position through *diffusion*. This is governed by the diffusion equation

$$\frac{\partial \rho}{\partial t} = \frac{\partial}{\partial z}\left(D \, \frac{\partial \rho}{\partial z}\right).$$

Here the diffusion coefficient D, according to the kinetic theory of gases, is

$$D = \frac{1}{3} v\lambda = \frac{1}{3} v(\nu) \frac{h}{p} \, l(\nu);$$

thus, in our problem, it is by no means a constant but depends upon p (or upon z) as well as on ν (or on the time).

We will now make a transformation from the variables t and z to the new variables ν and p with the help of the equations

$$dt = \frac{h}{p} \frac{l(\nu)}{v(\nu)} \, d\nu \quad \text{and} \quad p = p_0 e^{-z/h}. \tag{4}$$

The first equation is a consequence of the stopping theory, and the other is just the barometric height formula for an isothermal atmosphere. Then

$$\frac{\partial}{\partial t} = \frac{p}{h} \frac{v(\nu)}{l(\nu)} \frac{\partial}{\partial \nu} \quad \text{and} \quad \frac{\partial}{\partial z} = -\frac{p}{h} \frac{\partial}{\partial p},$$

so that the diffusion equation becomes

$$\frac{p}{h} \frac{v(\nu)}{l(\nu)} \frac{\partial \rho}{\partial \nu} = \frac{p}{h} \frac{\partial}{\partial p}\left(\frac{1}{3} \frac{h}{p} \, v(\nu)l(\nu) \frac{p}{h} \frac{\partial \rho}{\partial p}\right)$$

or in reduced form

$$\frac{\partial \rho}{\partial \nu} = \frac{1}{3} \, l(\nu)^2 \frac{\partial^2 \rho}{\partial p^2}. \tag{5}$$

c) If we measure p in atmospheres and put $p_0 = 1$, then the positions $p = 0$ and $p = 1$ are the upper and lower limits of the atmosphere. Besides the initial condition $\rho = \rho_0(p)$ for $\nu = 0$ we also have to formulate boundary conditions for both of these places before we can carry through the integration of the diffusion equation (5).

Of these the one for the upper limit of the atmosphere is immediately apparent: Since neutrons which reach the boundary can wander off to infinity, at that point $\rho = 0$. It is much more difficult to make a statement about the lower boundary. The neutrons penetrate into the rocks or into sea water where they are partly absorbed according to unknown laws but can be partly reflected with diminished velocity. Practically nothing can be said, therefore, about what takes place in the layers near the ground. A thorough discussion of what happens over an extended water surface is carried through in the work of Bethe, Korff and Placzek. We shall assume for the purpose of our calculation that the substances of the earth's surface absorb neutrons strongly, and we will put $\rho = 0$ for $p = 1$.

The solution of the differential equation (5) under these conditions can be put in the form of a Fourier series which is given by a slight extension of the classical theory of diffusion on account of the dependence of the parameter l on the variable ν:

$$\rho(\nu) = \sum_{n=1}^{\infty} A_n \sin n\pi p \; e^{-\pi^2 n^2 \cdot \frac{1}{3} \int_0^{\nu} l(\nu)^2 d\nu}, \qquad (6)$$

where the Fourier coefficients, A_n, determined from the initial condition $\rho(0) = \rho_0$, are

$$A_n = 2 \int_0^1 dp \rho_0(p) \sin n\pi p. \qquad (7)$$

d) In order to calculate the integral $\int_0^{\nu} l(\nu)^2 d\nu$, it is necessary to know l not only as a function of energy, according to equation (2), but also as a function of the number of collisions ν. Here we must investigate the stopping process somewhat more closely. We can say with a rather good approximation, that in an elastic collision a neutron of energy E, when colliding with an atom of mass M (expressed as a multiple of the neutron mass, or M = atomic weight) loses on the average an amount of energy

$$\Delta E = -\frac{2}{M + 1} E. \qquad (8a)$$

Hence

$$\frac{dE}{d\nu} = -\frac{2}{M + 1} E. \qquad (8b)$$

With the help of this relation we can convert the above integral to the energy scale in which l is given by equation (1). Thus we obtain

$$\int_0^{\nu} l(\nu)^2 d\nu = -\int_{E_0}^{E} l(E)^2 \frac{M + 1}{2} \frac{dE}{E} = \frac{M + 1}{2} \int_E^{E_0} l(E)^2 \frac{dE}{E}.$$

If we put $M = 14.6$ as the mean value for air then, in the case $E < E_s$, we get for the exponent of equation (6)

$$\frac{1}{3} \pi^2 n^2 \int_0^{\nu} l(\nu)^2 d\nu = n^2 10^{-6} \left\{ 8320 \log \frac{E_0}{E_s} + 174 \log \frac{E_s}{E} \right\}. \qquad (9)$$

e) We now ask how long and to what final energy does the stopping process persist before it is terminated in the absorption of the neutron in a $^{14}N(n,p)$ process. For this we can use the following formula: The fraction of neutrons of an initial energy E, which attain the energy E_2 without capture, is

$$\exp\left(-\int_{E_2}^{E_1} \frac{\sigma_{\text{abs}}}{\sigma_{\text{scat}} + \sigma_{\text{abs}}} \frac{dE}{|\Delta E|}\right), \tag{10}$$

where ΔE is the energy loss for each elastic collision, σ_{scat} is the effective cross-section for elastic collisions, and σ_{abs} is the concurrent (n,p) cross-section. With the help of equation (8), one obtains for the integral, neglecting σ_{abs} in the denominator,

$$\frac{M+1}{2}\int_{E_2}^{E_1} \frac{\sigma_{\text{abs}}}{\sigma_{\text{scat}}} \frac{dE}{E} = \frac{M+1}{2}\int_{E_2}^{\infty} \frac{0.16}{(E)^{\frac{1}{2}} \cdot 9.4} \frac{dE}{E} = \frac{0.266}{(E_2)^{\frac{1}{2}}}. \tag{11}$$

Thus, the energy E_2 is attained by the fraction $e^{-0.266/(E_2)^{1/2}}$ of the neutrons, or there is attained an energy

$E_2 =$	1	0.5	0.2	0.1	0.05	0.02	0.01 eV
by	77%	69%	55%	43%	30%	15%	7%

of all neutrons. In particular, the number of neutrons is reduced to $1/e$ of its original value for $E_2 = 0.07$ eV. Thus, the neutrons in the atmosphere do not quite reach thermal equilibrium; they become absorbed before they reach thermal energy. For an approximate description of the diffusion process it is sufficient to assume that all neutrons are absorbed at the same energy of 0.07 eV. or at a velocity of $V_2 = 3.7 \cdot 10^5$ cm./sec.

By means of the stopping theory we can, at least approximately, evaluate the time which elapses between the formation and the absorption of a neutron. From equation (3) and (8b) it follows that

$$\tau = \int_0^{v_2} dv \frac{h}{p} \frac{l(v)}{v(v)} = (M+1)h \int_{v_2}^{v_0} \frac{l(v)}{p} \frac{dv}{v^2}.$$

If one now defines p as the mean pressure within the region traversed by the neutron during its slowing down, then for $v_2 \ll v_S \ll v_0$ and with the use of equation (1) we get with good approximation

$$\tau = (M+1)\frac{h}{p} l(v_2)\frac{1}{v_2},$$

or in numbers

$$\tau = \frac{0.085}{\bar{p}} \sec. \tag{12}$$

where $\bar{p}$ is measured in atmospheres.

The mean life, in general, amounts to a few tenths of a second, and it increases to about 1 sec. only for $p = 0.1$ atm. Compared to the half value time of the neutron for β-decay of about 1 hour, this is such a short time that any notable influence of the β-instability (somewhat analogous to the meson) cannot come into the picture for the cosmic ray neutrons. In particular, it follows from this that the protons observed in the cosmic rays are certainly not formed from the neutrons but are either of primary origin or are formed by a process analogous to that by which the neutrons themselves are formed.

f) We can now get a firmer grasp on the question of the diffusion distribution. Since all measurements of neutrons have been made with the help of the $B(n,\alpha)$-reaction, we observe the neutrons only when they have reached the absorption range, that is, neutrons which already have the age τ. In equation (9) we can then put the final energy $E = 0.07$ eV. The value of E_s is difficult to give; it must lie between 10 and 150 keV. Since a more precise value is not possible, all further calculations will be carried through for the two extreme assumptions, where the equations designated by a) are for $E_s = 10$ keV and those with b) are for $E_s = 150$ keV. The numerical value for the exponential factor of equation (6) is

$$\exp\left(-n^2\pi^2 \cdot \frac{1}{3}\int_0^{\nu_s} l^2 d\nu\right) = E^{-0.00832n^2} \cdot 0.960^{n^2} \tag{13a}$$

$$= E^{-0.00832n^2} \cdot 0.982^{n^2}. \tag{13b}$$

We now write E instead of E_0 for the initial energy and measure it in MeV.

4. The Neutron Distribution in the Atmosphere

To calculate the Fourier coefficients A_n we have to make postulates about the source strength, or, in other words, about the radiation which excites the neutrons, and about the excitation process itself. Since in the greater expanse of the atmosphere an exponential decrease of neutron intensity is observed with increasing air pressure, it is plausible to try assigning to the primary radiation a uniform exponential decrease while it penetrates the atmosphere. Then $\rho_0 \sim e^{-\mu p}$, in which we should put $\mu \approx 7$.

Furthermore, we must make assumptions about the primary energy of the excited neutrons. We now know of one neutron excitation process which is observed in the atmosphere, namely, the Blau-Wambacher "stars" which were the subject of the preceding chapter. There we saw that their increase with elevation agrees well with the assumed increase of the number of neutrons present, for the frequency of the stars increases with elevation as e^{-7p}.

We know a little about the energy distribution in the stars. Two groups of emitted particles (protons and neutrons) are to be distinguished, an energetic group consisting of those particles which are struck directly by the primary ray and are ejected from the nucleus, and a low energy group of particles which are evaporated from the nucleus after its excitation. The observed distribution[1] can be best represented by the following superposition of two such distribution functions:

$$N(E)dE \sim E(a \cdot e^{-\alpha E} + b \cdot e^{-\beta E})dE.$$

$N(E)dE$ is the number of neutrons excited with an energy between E and $E + dE$; the constants have the numerical values:

$a = 0.178; b = 6.16$ (both in arbitrary intensity units); $\alpha = 0.08$ MeV^{-1} (corresponding to a half value breadth of the e-function of 8.6 MeV) and $\beta = 0.35$ MeV^{-1} (corresponding to a half value breadth of 2.0 MeV). We can then base our discussion on the statement:

$$\rho_0(p) = J_0 e^{-\mu p} E(ae^{-\alpha E} + be^{-\beta E})dE, \tag{14}$$

if we make the hypothesis that all neutrons are excited in the atmosphere by a primary radiation in Blau-Wambacher processes.

Introducing this statement into equation (7), the integration over p gives

$$2 \int_0^1 dp\, e^{-\mu p} \sin n\pi p = \frac{2n\pi[1 - e^{-\mu}(-1)^n]}{\mu^2 + n^2\pi^2}.$$

Since $\mu \approx 7$ the second term in the numerator will be omitted throughout. Thus one finally gets

$$\left.\begin{array}{c} \rho(p) = 2J_0 \sum_1^\infty \dfrac{n\pi}{\mu^2 + n^2\pi^2} \sin n\pi p \int_0^\infty E(ae^{-\alpha E} + be^{-\beta E})dE \times \\[2mm] \times\, 0.960^{n^2} E^{-0.00832 n^2}. \end{array}\right\} \tag{15a}$$

If the number 0.982 is used instead of 0.960 this formula goes over into (15b). The integrals which still remain in these equations can all be reduced to the Euler integral:

$$\int_0^\infty E^p e^{-\alpha E} dE = \frac{1}{\alpha^{p+1}} \int_0^\infty dx e^{-x} x^p = \frac{p!}{\alpha^{p+1}}. \tag{16}$$

---

[1]This distribution differs from the one given by BAGGE by the factor E which was introduced since one must suppose for theoretical reasons that the probability of evaporation will approach zero as $E \to 0$. To be sure, the experimental distribution function should have its maximum at a lower energy than is here assumed.

With this we finally obtain

$$\rho(p) = 2J_0 \sum_1^\infty \frac{n\pi}{\mu^2 + n^2\pi^2} \times$$

$$\times 0.960^{n^2} \left[\frac{a(1 - 0.00832n^2)!}{\alpha^{2-0.00832n^2}} + \frac{b(1 - 0.00832n^2)!}{\beta^{2-0.00832n^2}} \right] \sin n\pi p \qquad (17a)$$

and by replacing 0.960 by 0.982 we again get the corresponding equation (17b). These Fourier series are, moreover, semi-convergent; for as soon as $0.00832n^2 > 2$, or $n > 15$, the integral (16) no longer converges. The factor of the 15th term is, however, already very small and need not be considered further. Numerically, we get the two following Fourier equations:

for $E_s = 10$ keV:

$$\begin{aligned} \rho(p) = \ &3.64 \sin \pi p + 4.10 \sin 2\pi p + 2.96 \sin 3\pi p \\ &+ 1.791 \sin 4\pi p + 0.946 \sin 5\pi p + 0.455 \sin 6\pi p \\ &+ 0.199 \sin 7\pi p + 0.081 \sin 8\pi p + 0.031 \sin 9\pi p \\ &+ 0.011 \sin 10\pi p + 0.004 \sin 11\pi p + 0.001 \sin 12\pi p \end{aligned} \qquad (18a)$$

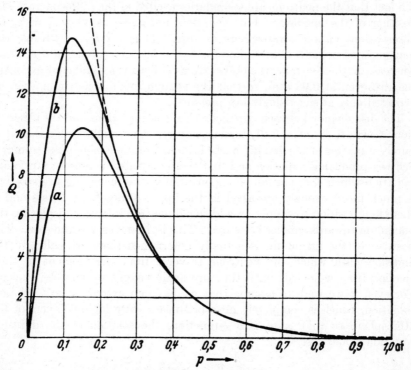

Figure 1. Theoretical distribution of slow neutrons in the atmosphere. a) $E_s = 10$ KeV; b) $E_s = 150$ KeV.

and for $E_S = 150$ keV:

$$\rho(p) = 4.26 \sin \pi p + 5.15 \sin 2\pi p + 4.19 \sin 3\pi p \\
+ 2.96 \sin 4\pi p + 1.910 \sin 5\pi p + 1.185 \sin 6\pi p \\
+ 0.696 \sin 7\pi p + 0.393 \sin 8\pi p + 0.220 \sin 9\pi p \\
+ 0.119 \sin 10\pi p + 0.066 \sin 11\pi p + 0.037 \sin 12\pi p. \tag{18b}$$

In these the arbitrary normalization is so chosen that for high pressures both functions go over approximately into $50 \cdot e^{-\mu p}$. The value of 7.07 has been used for μ in the computations.

The two functions are compared in Fig. 1 with the experimental points (the dotted line).

5. Discussion of the Maximum of the Neutron Density

One sees that both theoretical curves agree well towards the right side with the observed exponential decrease, corresponding to our postulate (14). The formation of a maximum is likewise a necessary consequence of the fact that the neutrons are secondaries excited in the atmosphere. The position of the maximum, however, does not agree at all well with the observations on the stratosphere ascents. Thus for $E_S = 10$ keV the maximum occurs at 0.15 atm., and for $E_S = 150$ keV it occurs at 0.12 atm., whereas, on the contrary, the observations still show a significant exponential rise even at 0.08 atm. so that the attainment of a maximum can be expected only at surprisingly low pressures.

The discrepancy between our theoretical considerations and the observations seems to be of a really serious nature. One might think that it is purely a matter of our having made false assumptions about the primary, neutron-producing radiation and that there may also be present a primary radiation which does not fall off exponentially with increasing pressure but is much more strongly absorbed in the upper atmospheric layers and is there in a position to supply an additional neutron intensity displacing the maximum towards smaller pressures. This is, however, not the case. The position of the maximum is actually determined more critically by the diffusion path which the neutrons traverse from the moment of their ejection from a nucleus until they are again caught by another nucleus. For even if we were to assume that we have an extremely soft primary radiation, which is completely absorbed in the very highest layers of the atmosphere so that $\rho_0(p)$ is a δ-function, the solution of the diffusion equation would give

$$\rho \sim \frac{p}{(\int l^2 dv)^{3/2}} e^{-3p^2/4 \int l^2 dv}. \tag{19}$$

This distribution would have a maximum at the point

$$p = \left(\frac{2}{3} \int l^2 d\nu\right)^{\frac{1}{2}} = \left(1690 \log \frac{E_0}{E_S} + 35 \log \frac{E_S}{E}\right)^{\frac{1}{2}} \cdot 10^{-3} \text{ atm.},$$

as is found by invoking equation (9). With $E = 0.07$ eV one obtains the following values.

With $E_0 =$	1 MeV	10 MeV
and (a) $E_S = $ 10 keV:	$p = 0.091$ atm.	$p = 0.110$ atm.
and (b) $E_S = 150$ keV:	$p = 0.061$ atm.	$p = 0.087$ atm.

One sees from this, in the first place, that other assumptions about the neutron-exciting component of the cosmic radiation do not change the discrepancy and, second, that a variation of the primary energy of the excited neutrons also effects no essential improvement in the situation. For these reasons any changes in the nuclear-physical postulates above an energy of 1 MeV are practically without significance as regards this question.

After their energy becomes less than E_S the neutrons, because of the increased scattering cross-section, cannot change their position appreciably; the diffusion path, therefore, consists largely of the path traversed during the slowing down from E_0 to E_S. A significant reduction of this length is thus only possible if E_0 is reduced nearly to E_S. The above numerical values show that the initial energy would have to be reduced to a few 100 keV, a situation which is very improbable from the nuclear physics point of view.

Even though the nuclear physics data which we have used may be quite uncertain, one gets the impression that even considerable alterations in these would not afford a solution to the difficulties. But one should still consider, as a last possibility, whether our assumption on the chemical constitution of the atmosphere is valid. In fact, at a height of 20 km. ($p = 0.055$ atm.) the ratio between N_2 and O_2 is displaced from its ground value of 78.1 : 20.9 to about 85 : 15.[1] A noticeable enrichment of H_2 and He should not yet be present. Since the elastic scattering cross-sections of nitrogen and of oxygen are not essentially different at energies above E_S, this displacement cannot change things much; even below E_S this only means an increase of the mean scattering cross-section from $9.2 \cdot 10^{-24}$ cm.^{2} per air atom on the ground to $9.7 \cdot 10^{-24}$ cm.^{2} (Our calculations have been based upon $9.4 \cdot 10^{-24}$ cm.).

---

[1] This would be true in the case of stratification for each component according to the barometric height formula. However, meteorologists incline to the assumption that in these altitudes complete mixing still prevails and the constitution of the air is the same as on the ground. Cf. R. PENNDORF, Meteor. Z **58** (1941) 1, 103.

The presence of water vapor in the lower atmospheric layers implies a reduction of the diffusion distance because of the much more rapid slowing down. That, however, does not change the form of the distribution curve, since the exponential decrease in the lower layers is independent of the diffusion distance and is determined by the absorption of the primary radiation as long as the diffusion distance is so small that no very considerable change of the neutron density $\rho(p)$ takes place over an interval of the order of magnitude of the diffusion distance. That is the case in the example which we have worked out and is naturally all the more correct if a mixture of water vapor shortens the diffusion distance still further. In the upper atmosphere, however, where this shortening could be of use to us, we have good reasons to assume that no water vapor is present.

GEOMAGNETIC EFFECTS

15. COSMIC RAYS AND THE MAGNETIC FIELD OF THE EARTH

By J. Meixner, Aachen

1. Statement of the Problem

The intensity of cosmic radiation is not the same over the whole surface of the earth. As Clay has discovered, it shows a definite correlation with the geomagnetic latitude; it varies only slightly along the geomagnetic equator. From this the conclusion is to be drawn that the magnetic field of the earth exerts an influence on cosmic radiation and that can be the case only if it consists at least in part, of electrically charged particles.

In order to compute the intensity of the cosmic radiation at various points on the earth's surface, one must have information about four things.

1. The magnetic field of the earth.
2. The directional distribution of cosmic radiation in external space.
3. The composition of cosmic radiation in external space.
4. The energy distribution of cosmic radiation in external space.

The magnetic field of the earth can be represented with good approximation as the field of a dipole with the moment $M = 8.1 \cdot 10^{25}$ gauss cm.^{3} It is about 340 km. from the center of the earth in 7° north geographic latitude and 160° west geographic longitude. Its direction runs from the magnetic south pole in the northern hemisphere to the magnetic north pole in the southern hemisphere.

The directional distribution of cosmic radiation in external space can be assumed as isotropic. According to all previous experience that is a useful working hypothesis.

No special assumptions will be made at first about the composition of the cosmic radiation and the energy distribution of its components.

Under these assumptions the following mathematical problem can now be stated. With a given composition and energy distribution in external space what are the composition and energy distribution (and thus the intensity) of cosmic radiation as it is incident from a definite direction on a definite point of the earth's surface?

From comparison of the solution of this problem with measurements of cosmic radiation at the earth's surface and in the atmosphere, conclusions can be drawn about the characteristics of cosmic radiation in external space.

2. Application of Liouville's Theorem

Here we shall consider only one component of cosmic radiation and of this only one segment of the energy spectrum between the energies E and $E + dE$ or with velocities between v and $v + dv$. The number of particles in a volume element $dxdydz$ with velocities between v and $v + dv$ and with direction of motion in the solid angle $d\Omega$ is

$$I \cdot dx \, dy \, dz \, dv \, d\Omega. \tag{1}$$

The factor I is a measure of the intensity at the position xyz in the solid angle $d\Omega$. In external space I, according to our assumption, is independent of direction and position. It can be shown then that within the region of the earth's magnetic field the same is true at every place and in every direction in which particles of the given kind and velocity can occur at all. The proof rests upon a slight modification of Liouville's Theorem of statistical mechanics (Fermi and Rossi (F 2); Swann (S 24)). The equations of motion for a particle of kinetic mass m and charge e, (measured in electrostatic units) in a magnetic field H (in gauss) are

$$\frac{d}{dt}(m\vec{v}) = \frac{e}{c}\left[\vec{v},\vec{H}\right]; \qquad \vec{v} = \frac{d\vec{r}}{dt}. \tag{2}$$

$\vec{r}$ is the radius vector with components x, y, z. The scalar value of the velocity and hence the kinetic mass remain constant during the motion in a magnetic field. Therefore

$$\dot{\vec{v}} = \frac{d\vec{v}}{dt} = \frac{e}{mc}\left[\vec{v},\vec{H}\right]; \qquad \dot{\vec{r}} = \vec{v}. \tag{3}$$

From this it follows that

$$\frac{\partial \dot{v}_x}{\partial v_x} + \frac{\partial \dot{v}_y}{\partial v_y} + \frac{\partial \dot{v}_z}{\partial v_z} + \frac{\partial \dot{x}}{\partial x} + \frac{\partial \dot{y}}{\partial y} + \frac{\partial \dot{z}}{\partial z} = 0. \tag{4}$$

If we introduce a six dimensional position-velocity space with the coordinate x, y, z, v_x, v_y, v_z (in the usual Liouville theorem a phase space is used instead of this), then (4) implies that the divergence of the six dimensional velocity vector with components $\dot{x}, \dot{y}, \dot{z}, \dot{v}_x, \dot{v}_y, \dot{v}_z$, vanishes and that, therefore, the flow governed by the equations of motion (3) is incompressible in the position-velocity space. Moreover, since $dxdydzdvd\Omega$, except for a constant factor v^2, is exactly the size of an elementary cell in position-velocity space, this remains constant during the flow, and the intensity is always the same wherever the flow goes.

It remains only to investigate where the flow goes, namely to what points and from what directions (or with what velocity components v_x, v_y, v_z)

particles of velocity v can arrive at a given observation point x,y,z from external space or from infinity. One is therefore concerned with the determination of those orbits described by the equations of motion (3) which arrive at the observation point from infinity.

In connection with the theory of the aurora this problem was thoroughly studied by Störmer. The calculations were extended for the special purposes of cosmic ray investigations by Störmer and, particularly, by Lemaitre, Vallarta, and their coworkers.

3. The Equations of Motion in the Magnetic Field of the Earth

After the magnetic field of the dipole is inserted in the equations of motion (3), they can be put in a form in which the physical quantities M, m,e,v and t no longer appear explicitly. To this end the arc length $s = vt$ is introduced instead of the time as independent variable, and the interval

$$\left(\frac{\pm eM}{mvc}\right)^{\frac{1}{2}}.\tag{5}$$

is chosen as the unit of length. This will be designated as the Störmer unit of length or as 1 störmer. The upper sign is for use with positive particles and the lower sign with negative particles. This unit of length is different for each velocity or energy; since, in the case of cosmic ray particles, we generally have to deal with velocities near the velocity of light the unit of length is almost inversely proportional to the square root of the kinetic mass m or of the energy mc^2 of the particle.

If polar coordinates r_1,λ,φ are introduced (r_1 = distance from the magnetic center of the earth measured in störmers; λ = geomagnetic latitude, positive north of the geomagnetic equator, φ = geomagnetic longitude increasing from east to west) then the equations of motion referred to the arc length s instead of the time and to störmer units of length are

$$\frac{d^2r_1}{ds^2} - r_1\cos^2\lambda\left(\frac{d\varphi}{ds}\right)^2 - r_1\left(\frac{d\lambda}{ds}\right)^2 = \mp\frac{\cos^2\lambda}{r_1^2}\frac{d\varphi}{ds}\;;\tag{6}$$

$$r_1\frac{d^2\lambda}{ds^2} + 2\frac{dr_1}{ds}\frac{d\lambda}{ds} + r_1\sin\lambda\cos\lambda\left(\frac{d\varphi}{ds}\right)^2 = \mp\frac{2\sin\lambda\cos\lambda}{r_1^2}\frac{d\varphi}{ds}\;;\tag{7}$$

$$\frac{d}{ds}\left(r_1^2\cos^2\lambda\frac{d\varphi}{ds}\right) - \mp\frac{d}{ds}\left(\frac{\cos^2\lambda}{r_1}\right).\tag{8}$$

Two integrals can be obtained immediately. From (8) it follows that

$$r_1^2\cos^2\lambda\cdot\frac{d\varphi}{ds} = \mp\left(\frac{\cos^2\lambda}{r_1} - 2\gamma_1\right).\tag{9}$$

The constant of integration γ_1 is proportional to the component of angular momentum parallel to the magnetic moment of the earth at infinite particle distance. It can assume all values between $-\infty$ and $+\infty$. The conservation of energy gives the integral

$$\left(\frac{dr_1}{ds}\right)^2 + r_1^2\left(\frac{d\lambda}{ds}\right)^2 + r_1^2 \cos^2 \lambda \left(\frac{d\varphi}{ds}\right)^2 = 1. \tag{10}$$

The right side of the equation is unity since we are differentiating with respect to the arc s instead of the time. $d\varphi/ds$ can be eliminated from the equations (6), (7), (9) and (10). Then we have a system of two differential equations and the accompanying energy integral for the coordinates r_1 and λ. If these are integrated, the φ-component of the motion is given by (9). Thus, the motion in the field of a magnetic dipole is separated into the motion in the meridian plane and the motion of the meridian plane about the dipole axis.

For numerical calculations it is convenient to portray the meridian plane in a plane with the rectangular coordinates x,λ with respect to which the angles are undistorted and in which x is defined for positive γ_1, according to Störmer, by

$$2\gamma_1 r_1 = e^x. \tag{11}$$

As a new independent variable, σ is chosen and defined by $(2\gamma_1)^3 ds = e^{2x} d\sigma$.

The equations of motion in x and λ are now

$$\frac{d^2 x}{d\sigma^2} = \frac{1}{2}\frac{\partial P}{\partial x} \;; \qquad \frac{d^2\lambda}{d\sigma^2} = \frac{1}{2}\frac{\partial P}{\partial \lambda}, \tag{12}$$

where

$$P(x,\lambda) \equiv a e^{2x} - \left(e^{-x}\cos\lambda - \frac{1}{\cos\lambda}\right)^2 \;; \qquad a = (2\gamma_1)^{-4}. \tag{13}$$

The energy integral is

$$\left(\frac{dx}{d\sigma}\right)^2 + \left(\frac{d\lambda}{d\sigma}\right)^2 - P(x,\lambda) = 0. \tag{14}$$

The equations (12) can thus be interpreted as the equations of motion of a particle of mass 2 under the influence of a conservative force with the potential $-P(x,\lambda)$ in a plane with rectangular coordinates x,λ. The total energy of this motion, according to (14), however, is not arbitrary but has the fixed value zero. From the contour diagram of the function P one can get an approximate idea of the course of the motion in the meridian plane (cf. Fig. 2).[1]

---

[1] The motion also takes place in the meridian plane as though a conservative force were acting in it. Contour diagrams of the potentials corresponding to various values of r_1 may be found in Störmers papers (S 20).

If x and λ are known as functions of σ, or s, then the direction of the orbit in space is also given. The angle θ, which the trajectory in space makes with the meridian plane, will be regarded as positive if the orbit passes through the meridian plane in the direction of increasing φ; thus, $\sin \theta$ is equal to the φ-component of a unit vector in the direction of the velocity, or, according to (9) and (11),

$$\pm \sin \theta = \pm r_1 \cos \lambda \frac{d\varphi}{ds} = \frac{2\gamma_1}{r_1 \cos \lambda} - \frac{\cos \lambda}{r_1^2} = \left(1 - \frac{P}{a} e^{-2x}\right)^{\frac{1}{2}}. \quad (15)$$

If η is the angle which the orbit in the meridian plane makes with the radius drawn to the center of the earth, then

$$\tan \eta = r\frac{d\lambda}{dr} = \frac{d\lambda}{dx}. \quad (16)$$

4. The Störmer Cone

A point on the orbit and the tangent at that point are given by the coordinates r_1, λ, φ and by the angles θ and η. For observation points on the surface of the earth these quantities are designated by $r_{10}, \lambda_0, \varphi_0, \theta_0, \eta_0$. If r_0 is the radius of the earth in cms. then from (5)

$$r_0 = r_{10} \cdot \left(\frac{\pm eM}{mvc}\right)^{\frac{1}{2}}. \quad (17)$$

Since r_0, e, M and the rest mass of the particle are all previously known quantities, then r_{10}, the magnitude of the earth's radius in störmers, is a measure of the energy of the particle. For velocities near the velocity of light r_{10} is nearly proportional to the root of the particle energy. Table I gives this relation between r_{10} and the energy for electrons, protons and α-particles (from Lemaitre and Vallarta (L 6)).

We now consider the orbits belonging to a fixed value of γ_1. They can fill only that part of the meridian plane for which $P \geq 0$, or $|\sin \theta| \leq 1$. Fig. 1 shows the curves $P = 0$ in the x, λ-plane for various values of r_1 between 0.78854 and 1. For negative λ the diagram is the mirror image of Fig. 1 about the line $\lambda = 0$. For $\gamma_1 < 1$ the region allowed for the orbits is simply connected, for $\gamma_1 > 1$ there are two allowed regions separated from each other. For $\gamma_1 = 1$ the two regions have just one point in common at $x = 0.693$, $\lambda = 0$.

Table 1.

r_{10}	Kinetic energy in Billion e-volts for		
	electrons	protons	α-particles
0.1	0.596	0.172	0.184
0.2	2.38	1.62	2.31
0.3	5.36	4.49	7.60
0.4	9.54	8.61	15.64
0.5	14.9	14.0	26.25
0.6	21.5	20.5	39.28
0.7	29.1	28.2	54.6
0.8	38.2	37.2	72.5
0.9	48.3	47.3	92.7
1.0	59.6	58.5	115.2

For one of the allowed regions $r_1 < 1$, and for the other $r_1 > 1$. An orbit which comes from infinity with $\gamma_1 > 1$ can reach no points with $r_1 < 1$; hence particles whose energy corresponds to $r_{10} < 1$ cannot reach the surface of the earth from infinity. The critical value $\gamma_1 = 1$ corresponds, at a given observation point r_{10}, λ_0, according to (15), to all directions with the critical angle θ_0, or to a circular cone with axis perpendicular to the meridian plane. Therefore, into this circular cone, with angle of opening depending

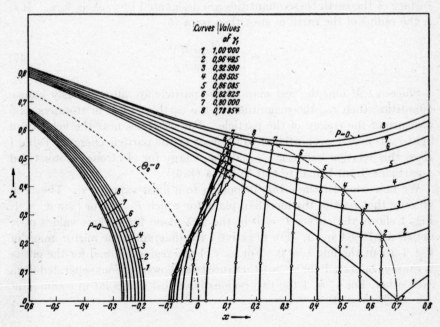

Figure 1. Curves $P = 0$, inner stable and outer unstable periodic orbits for various values of γ, (according to Baños, Uribe, and Lifschitz (B 5)).

upon the observation point, no particles can succeed in arriving from infinity. It is designated as the Störmer cone (Störmer (S 20)). The forbidden directions are in the east for positive particles and in the west for negative.

The left branch of the curve $P = 0$, which cuts the equator perpendicularly, backs off in the x, λ-plane towards smaller values of x as γ_1 diminishes, or, conversely, towards larger values of r_1 if one transforms from x to r_1 by means of (11). The branch of the curve $P = 0$ for $\gamma_1 = 1$, therefore, constitutes an absolute lower limit of r_1 for particles coming from infinity. The corresponding energies for electrons, protons, and α-particles are listed in table 2 as calculated from equation (17). According to this, for example, no protons from infinity can succeed in reaching the earth's surface in geomagnetic latitude 30° if their energy is less than $5.2 \cdot 10^9$ eV. This lower limit can, in general, be more precisely defined for definite directions of observation.

Table 2.

λ_0	γ_{10}	Lower limit of kinetic energy in 10^9 e-volts for		
		electrons	protons	α-particles
0°	0.414	10.2	9.30	17.0
10°	0.404	9.73	8.81	16.0
20°	0.375	8.38	7.48	13.4
30°	0.328	6.41	5.23	9.60
40°	0.266	4.22	3.37	5.48
50°	0.194	2.24	1.49	2.10
60°	0.121	0.87	0.24	0.39
70°	0.058	0.20	0.021	0.021
80°	0.014	0.011	$0.72 \cdot 10^{-4}$	$0.73 \cdot 10^{-4}$
90°	0.000	0	0	0

5. General Properties of the Orbits

If nothing is said to the contrary, all of the following discussion is concerned with motion in the meridian plane, or in the x, λ-plane. The orbits can be traced in both directions, (a statement which does not apply to the spatial orbits), since the equations of motion (12) are not altered if $-\sigma$ is substituted for σ. Instead of speaking of orbits which come from infinity and pass through the point of observation, one can, therefore, speak about orbits which go out from the point of observation to infinity.

The equations of motion (12) appear not to be integrable in closed form. For their treatment there has been recourse to general theorems (Schremp (S 13)); to series expansions (Baños (B 2, 4, 5); Bouckaert (B 31), Godart (G 5, 8); Lemaitre (L 4); Lemaitre and Vallarta (L 7); Schremp (S 14); Störmer (S 21); Yong-Li (Y 1) and to numerical methods (Hutner (H 14, 16); Lemaitre and Vallarta (L 8, 9); Schremp (S 14); Störmer (S 21)).

In order to give an insight into the possible types of orbits the contour diagram of Fig. 2 for $\gamma_1 = 0.89$ will first be mentioned. Along the line $P = $ const. the kinetic energy of the two dimensional motion in the meridian plane is equal to P. The relief of the potential energy $-P$, corresponding to the contour lines, is very flat over a relatively large region around $r_1 = 0.69$ $(x = 0.2)$ (the function has a flat maximum of amount 0.1163 at $x = 0.204$, $\lambda = 0$; the maximum vanishes for $\gamma_1 < 0.8774$). For $x < -0.23$ the allowed region with $P \geq 0$ consists, in relief, of two grooves becoming

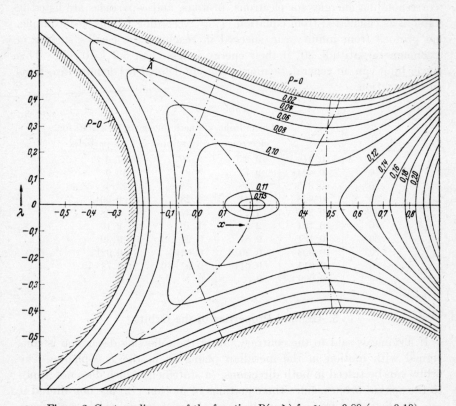

Figure 2. Contour diagram of the function $P(x, \lambda)$ for $\gamma_1 = 0.89$ $(a = 0.10)$.

ever narrower towards the left and sloping off gently towards the right and, with diminishing x, extending into greater and greater latitudes. For larger values of x of about 0.6 and greater, an exponential variation of the relief begins; the term ae^{2x} in (13) is responsible for this.

Since the unit in which r_1 is measured (the zero point of the x coordinate) depends on the particle energy, the position of the earth's surface in this diagram according to (17) also depends upon the particle energy. The surface of the earth comes at $x_0 = -0.34$, $+ 0.065$ and $+ 0.54$ (i.e. $r_{10} =$ 0.4, 0.6, 0.962) for electrons of energy 9.5, 21.5 and 56 BeV respectively. An orbit which goes towards the right from $x_0 = 0.54$ ($r_{10} = 0.962 = (\gamma_1)^{\frac{2}{3}}$) in an arbitrary direction always experiences an acceleration to the right and can, therefore, never return again to the initial value of x_0, i.e., it cannot come back to the earth's surface in any latitude. Only in the region between the two dot-dash curves is the x-component of the acceleration directed to the left, i.e. $\partial P / \partial x < 0$. Therefore, for $r_{10} > 0.962$ all direc-

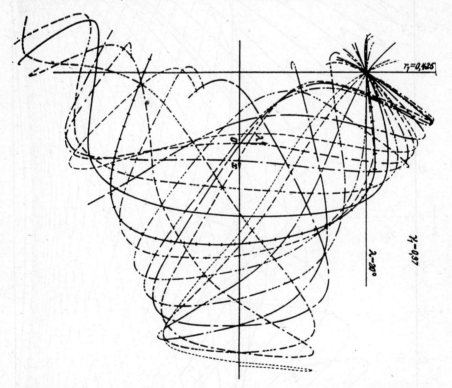

Figure 3. Family of orbits which start out from one point. (According to HUTNER (H 14)).

tions are allowed. A corresponding limit also exists for all other positive values of $\gamma_1 < 1$.—An orbit which starts out in any accessible latitude from $x_0 = 0.065$ can spend more or less time, according to its initial direction, in the flat region around $x = 0.2$ and thus oscillate in the x- as well as in the λ-direction (cf. Fig. 3); under certain circumstances it can take on smaller values of x than the initial value x_0 before it finally succeeds in passing out towards infinity. Such an orbit should be excluded since its course lies partly inside the earth and, therefore, would lie in the earth's

shadow. In the case of a large number of oscillations rather small differences in the initial direction can lead to very different orbital positions. As a
closer investigation shows, this means that there is a series of directional

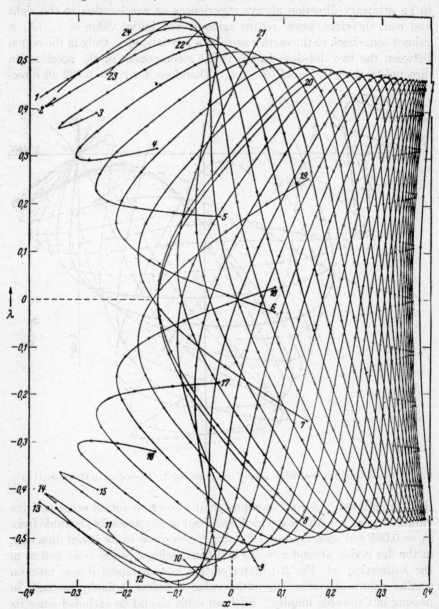

Figure 4. Family of asymptotic orbits for $\gamma_1 = 0.85$. (According to Baños (B 2)).

regions within which the orbits extend to infinity without intersecting the earth; between these lie other directional regions forbidden by the shadow effect of the earth. There are also orbits which do not extend to infinity at all; to these belong the periodic orbits (cf. Fig. 1) and such orbits as start out from the position of observation and approach asymptotically to a periodic orbit (cf. Fig. 4).—An orbit which starts out from $x_0 = -0.34$ towards the right will first follow the groove and can then execute a series of oscillations in the flat region around $x = 0.2$; but here it turns out that only for a few initial directions will the orbit get back into the groove and return to $x < -0.34$, thus intersecting the earth, before it again runs out along the groove. In general, the orbit will find its way to infinity before it does this. The smaller the energy of the particle, the farther to the left the earth's surface is to be taken, and the more rarely will the orbit find its way back. Since with diminishing x_0 the groove extends to ever greater latitudes, this implies that in high latitudes nearly all directions are allowed, and practically the only forbidden directions lie within the simple shadow cone (see below).

For smaller γ_1 the coefficient a in (13) becomes greater, and this means that the region of the sharp slope of the relief extends more and more to the left. For $\gamma_1 < 0.78854$ there are no oscillations[1] and, therefore, no more periodic orbits. In spite of this, certain directions still remain forbidden, e.g., all orbits which start out towards the north near the horizon from point A (Fig. 2). As can be seen immediately from the contour diagram, they will be curved towards the left and will thus intersect the earth before they can escape to infinity. With such orbits one speaks of the simple shadow effect (Schremp (S 14)).

A general discussion of the orbits leads to the following results (Schremp (S 13, 14)).

1. For $r_{10} > 1$ all directions are allowed for any value of γ_1 either positive or negative. The intensity of cosmic radiation for the corresponding energies (cf. table 1) is the same in all directions at the place of observation and equal to that in external space. It is therefore insensitive to the magnetic field.

2. For $r_{10} < 1$ all directions in the Störmer cone, i.e. with $\gamma_1 > 1$, are forbidden.

3. For $r_{10} < 1$ all directions with $-\infty < \gamma_1 < r_{10}^3$ are allowed and the appropriate value of θ_0 is to be calculated from (15).

4. For $r_{10}^3 < \gamma_1 < 0.78854$ only the simple shadow cone comes into

---

[1]For the general discussion of orbits from the topological point of view it is convenient to introduce the concept of the number of oscillations. A section of an orbit at both ends of which the kinetic energy is a minimum is designated as an oscillation or a reentrant orbital section (Schremp (S 13)).

consideration. The directions forbidden by it and by the Störmer cone
have been given by Schremp (S 14) for all latitudes and energies.

5. The most complicated behavior occurs for $r_{10} < (\gamma_1)^{\frac{1}{3}}$ in the region
$0.78854 < \gamma_1 < 1$.

This is already shown in Figs. 1 and 3. But even in this range of r_1 all
orbits from the observation point lead out to infinity except for a quantitatively insignificant group; where as for $\gamma_1 < 0.78854$ there are no oscillations, these can take place any large number of times for $0.78854 < \gamma_1 < 1$,
thus bringing about a complicated shadow effect.

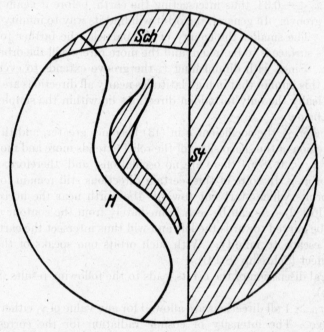

Figure 5. Schematic diagram of allowed and forbidden directions.

For the purpose of displaying the allowed and forbidden directions for
any given point of observation, one can plot the quantities $\sin \theta_0$ and
$\cos \theta_0 \sin \eta_0$ for each direction in a rectangular coordinate system. This
diagram can also be obtained if each orbit is allowed to intersect a unit
sphere drawn about the observation point and these points of intersection
are projected upon the horizontal plane. Fig. 5 gives such a schematic
diagram for the allowed and forbidden directional regions and Fig. 6 gives
the calculated diagram for a definite case.

The allowed and forbidden regions are separated by critical directions
or orbits; there are two kinds of these, but both depend upon the shadow

effect of the earth. The critical orbits of the first kind start out from the point of observation, and from the inside they approach asymptotically to one of the outer periodic orbits of Fig. 1 (cf. Fig. 4); these outer periodic orbits exist only for $0.78854 < \gamma_1 < 1$ and, in contrast to the inner periodic orbits, which exist for $0.78854 < \gamma_1 < \infty$, they are unstable.[1] The critical orbits of the second kind start out from the observation point, come back again to the earth's surface and just touch it before executing a more or less large number of oscillations outside the earth and then passing out to infinity. Such orbits occur for $r_{10}^3 < \gamma_1 < 1$.

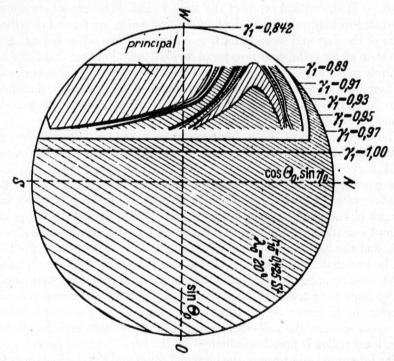

Figure 6. Diagram of allowed and forbidden directions. Positive particles, northern hemisphere. White area was not calculated. (According to Hutner (H 14)).

In the schematic diagram of Fig. 5 the forbidden Störmer cone (limit St) lies to the right. It extends to the value of θ_0 given by equation (15) for the λ_0 and r_{10} of the observation point and $\gamma_1 = 1$. To the left is a connected allowed region. It is made up of the so-called principal cone, reduced by the

[1] Besides these periodic orbits there are also other complicated patterns; diagrams of such are to be found in the work of Störmer (S 20) and Hutner (H 15). If an orbit in the meridian plane is periodic the three dimensional spatial orbit is, in general, not closed; orbits closed in space were studied by Godart (G 8).

segment of the simple shadow cone (limit *Sch*), which juts into it. Between the limits *H*, *Sch*, *St* is the so-called half shadow region or penumbra. In this there are an infinite number of alternately allowed and forbidden strips (cf. Fig. 6); in the schematic diagram just one forbidden strip is shown.

All directions for which the orbits go to infinity from the observation point without oscillation lie within the principal cone. In the region common to the principal cone and the simple shadow cone the orbits intersect the earth before they go to infinity. The edge of the principal cone is formed of the critical orbits of the first kind; that of the simple shadow cone is formed of the critical orbits of the second kind. The edges between allowed and forbidden strips in the half-shadow region are formed of critical orbits of the first and second kinds, respectively. The orbits belonging to each strip all have the same number of oscillations. The fact that there are infinitely many allowed and forbidden strips is immediately connected with the fact that there are orbits with any number of oscillations (infinitely many in the case of periodic orbits and those asymptotic to the periodic orbits) (Schremp (S 13)).

The computation of the half-shadow regions has been carried through for 20° latitude by Hutner (H 1) and for the magnetic equator by Yong-Li (Y 1).

In general, the following qualitative statements can be made about the structure of the allowed and forbidden directions. For low latitudes and energies in the neighborhood of $r_{10} = 1$ all of the allowed directions are reduced essentially to the principal cone; the half-shadow region is almost dark, and the half-shadow cone is very small. For intermediate latitudes and intermediate energies (r_{10} between about 0.35 and 0.5) the structure is the most complex; in the half-shadow region the forbidden strips again predominate over the allowed; this can lead to large variations or a fine structure in the directional distribution of cosmic rays. For large latitudes and small energies the half-shadow region is almost light and the allowed directional region is practically limited by the simple shadow cone.

The integrated apertures of the principal cones and the shadow cones for all energies and latitudes have been assembled by Koenig (K 2).

6. The Geomagnetic Effect of Cosmic Radiation

When the diagram of allowed and forbidden directions has been computed for all energies at a given observation point, one can read from it what energies are allowed at a given point of the diagram corresponding to a given direction of observation. In Fig. 7 the allowed energies for $\lambda_0 = 20°$ are given for those directions which are inclined 60° from the zenith. This holds for positive particles; and for negative particles $-\theta_0$ is to be substituted for θ. The lower limit of the allowed energies lies above $r_{10} = 0.375$ as it must in this latitude, according to table 2. For directions from north to west and somewhat beyond, the half-shadow region is shown as a series of allowed and forbidden energy regions beyond which, from the limit of the region corresponding to the principal cone, an uninterrupted allowed energy spectrum comes in.

In order to obtain the incident intensity for positive particles in a definite direction, one must integrate the energy spectrum $j^+(E)$ of these particles in external space over all allowed energies. The result of this integration is shown in Fig. 8 for three different assumptions about the

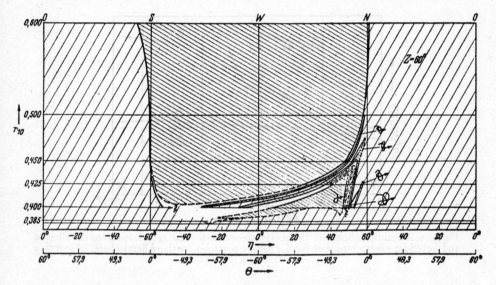

Figure 7. The allowed and forbidden energies (expressed in r_{10}) at zenith angle $z = 60°$ for various azimuths. The orbital type is given by the figures at the right of the allowed strips. Positive particles, northern hemisphere. (According to Hutner (H 16)).

energy spectrum. For the assumption $j^+(E) \sim E^{-2\cdot8}$, which is suggested by the behavior of the hard component in the atmosphere, jagged variations of the intensity occur for variations of azimuth at constant zenith angle between the north and west. They are an immediate consequence of the existence of the half-shadow regions. Such variations are designated as the fine structure of cosmic ray intensity. Its existence is confirmed by a series of observations (Cooper (C 8, 9), Ribner (R 3, 4), Schremp (S 15), Schremp and Ribner (S 16)). Magnetic disturbances seem to influence these strongly (Schremp (S 15)). Because of the strong dependence of the fine structure on the assumed energy spectrum, which is shown in Fig. 8, fine structure studies should be especially suited to the determination of

the energy spectrum of the primary particles of cosmic radiation; of first
importance are investigations at constant zenith angle and variable azimuth,
since then the effect of the atmosphere on the primary particles is the same
for all directions because of the nearly equal absorption path for all directions (Vallarta (V 4)).[1]

Besides the azimuthal effect mentioned, the following geomagnetic
effects of cosmic radiation are of interest: The latitude effect, the north-
south asymmetry, the east-west asymmetry, the longitude effect and the
effect of magnetic disturbances.

For a qualitative discussion, at least for low altitudes, one can limit him-

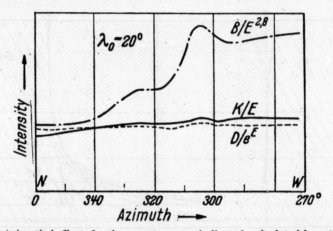

Figure 8. Azimuthal effects for the energy spectra indicated, calculated from the allowed
and forbidden energy ranges of Fig. 7. Positive particles, northern hemisphere. (According
to HUTNER (H 16)).

self to the principal cone diminished by the segment of the simple shadow
cone which juts into it. (Lemaitre and Vallarta) (L 9) have given (a)
the principal cone for $\lambda_0 = 0°$, $20°$, $30°$, and all energies, (b) the critical
energies in these latitudes for the zenith angle $45°$, and (c) the critical
energies in the zenith directions for all latitudes.) Then at each observation
point and at each direction there are a critical value $r_k(\lambda_0, \theta_0, n_0)$ of r_{10} and a
corresponding critical energy. Above this all energies are allowed, and below
it all are forbidden. For the directions in the north-south and in the east-

---

[1]This is not exactly right since the orbits are curved in the magnetic field. For
protons and electrons of 10 BeV whose paths lie in the equatorial plane, the radius of
curvature at the earth's surface is about 1000 km and that makes a difference in the
absorption paths in an atmosphere of 100 km thickness of 14 km at $45°$, and of 30 km
at $60°$ zenith angle.

west planes the critical values are given in Fig. 9 for the case of positive particles in geomagnetic latitude 30°. For negative particles the curves E and W are to be interchanged, and for −30° latitude the curves N and S are to be interchanged. If the velocity v lies close to the velocity of light, then from (17) the critical energy in electron volts is

$$E_k^{\pm} = 300M \frac{r_k^{\pm 2}}{r_0^2}. \tag{18}$$

The upper sign pertains to positive and the lower to negative particles. The critical energy, besides depending on $\lambda_0, \theta_0, \eta_0$, also depends on the magnetic moment M (in gauss cm.³) and on the distance r_0 (in cms.) of the observation point from the magnetic center of the earth. If the cosmic rays in external space consist of positive particles with the energy spectrum $j^+(E)$, of negative particles with $j^-(E)$, and of a neutral component of total

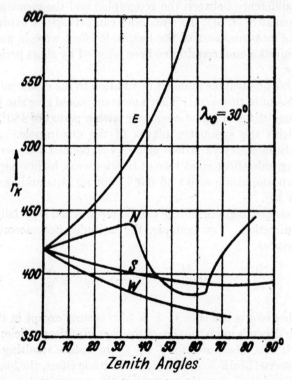

Figure 9. Critical energies (expressed in r_{10}) for the north-south and the east-west asymmetries. Positive particles, northern hemisphere. The rise of the N-curve for large zenith angles is due to the simple shadow cone. (According to LEMAITRE and VALLARTA (L 9)).

intensity K, then the intensity in a given direction at the observation point is given by

$$j = \int_{E_k^+}^{\infty} j(E)dE + \int_{E_k^-}^{\infty} j(E)dE + K. \tag{19}$$

The geomagnetic effect depends upon the change of the lower limit of these integrals when the parameters r_0, λ_0, θ_0, η_0, and M change.

Along the geomagnetic equator $E_k^{\rightarrow}$ changes only by the longitude variation of r_0; the geographic and the geomagnetic center of the earth do not coincide. j should thus have a maximum where r_0 is greatest at a point west of Africa. Along the geomagnetic equator the observed intensity has a period of 360° with amplitude agreeing qualitatively with the theory (Vallarta (V 2)). However, the maximum occurs at a point west of South America (Vallarta (V 3)). The source of this discrepancy is to be found in part in the difference between the geographic and the geomagnetic zenith direction (Lemaitre (L 5)); the remainder can perhaps be explained by the fact that the measurements of the longitude effect were in many cases of only short duration and could have been affected by short period magnetic disturbances.

A noticeable quadrupole moment in addition to the dipole moment seems not to be present in the earth. Such a moment would give rise to a variable intensity along the geomagnetic equator with a period of 180°, with nodes coinciding with the symmetry planes of the quadrupole. A harmonic analysis of the intensity variations gives a well defined 360° period of about 4% (the longitude effect cited above) besides weak higher harmonic functions with an amplitude of 0.1 to 0.3%, but no outstanding 180° period (Vallarta (V 6)).

The various geomagnetic effects can be represented especially simply for the zenith direction. For example, the latitude effect according to (18) and (19) becomes

$$\frac{\partial j}{\partial \lambda_0} = -600 \frac{M}{r_0^2} \left[j^+(E_k^+) + j^-(E_k^-) \right] r_k^{\rightarrow} \frac{\partial r_k^{\rightarrow}}{\partial \lambda}.$$

In the other effects the sum $j^+ + j^-$ also occurs, except in the east-west effect, which depends upon the sign of the charge of the particle; here $j^+ - j^-$ comes in. If one substitutes for $j^+ + j^-$ the values resulting in sequence from the observed north-south effect, the latitude effect, the longitude effect and the effect of the magnetic moment in the expression

$$\beta = \frac{j^+(E_k^+) + j^-(E_k^-)}{j^+(E_k^+) - j^-(E_k^-)} \tag{20}$$

Table 3.

$j^+ + j^-$ from	β	latitude	Height of atmosphere in m water equivalent
North-south asymmetry . . .	0.8 ± 0.3	$30°$	6 m H_2O
Latitude effect	1.16 ± 0.5	$30°$	10 m H_2O
Longitude effect	4.6	$0°$	10 m H_2O
$\partial j/\partial M$	170	$0°$	10 m H_2O

whereas, for $j^+ - j^-$, one substitutes the value resulting from the east-west effect, four independent determinations are obtained for each latitude. Table 3 contains the results taken from Johnson's work (J 9, 10, 11).

The first two results are completely compatible. According to them, j^+ must be essentially greater than j^- so that the cosmic radiation observed on the earth's surface behind 6 to 10 meters water equivalent must be derived in the main from positive primaries. One should not attribute too much significance to the number 4.6 resulting from the longitude effect since in the longitude effect, as already pointed out, there are other discrepancies of an unexplained origin. The value $\beta = 170$, resulting from the intensity variations during magnetic storms, has only formal significance; in its derivation it is assumed that one can describe these disturbances by a dipole field, variable in time, and this assumption is certainly not correct.

Thus, whereas the primary particles which are responsible for the geomagnetic effects at sea level carry a predominantly positive charge, it results from measurements of the geomagnetic effects at great heights (up to 0.33 m. H_2O) in the same way that $j^- = 44\%$, and $j^+ = 56\%$; that is, the primary particles which produce the effects at great heights are positive and negative with nearly equal frequency (Johnson (J 10)).

After invoking other considerations Johnson deduces from his results the following conclusions: (Johnson (J 8, 10, 12)):

1. The hard component of cosmic radiation in the atmosphere, which consists of mesons, is excited by primary protons.

2. The soft component, which contributes the main portion of the cosmic rays in the upper atmosphere, is excited by electrons which are charged positively and negatively with equal frequency. They excite cascade showers. The field sensitive part of these electrons with energies of less than 60 BcV is completely absorbed in the atmosphere; therefore, this component can have no geomagnetic effects at sea level.

3. Cosmic radiation in external space is on the average electrically neutral. That is understandable as was pointed out by Swann, inasmuch as gigantic potential differences would occur between relatively closely spaced points in interstellar space if an appreciable fraction of cosmic radiation

should not be neutralized on the average, and this would be inconsistent with the observed passage of charged particles through space.

The observations on the latitude effect of large showers are worthy of note. Jesse and Gill (J 6) and Schein and Gill (S 2) find a considerable dependence on latitude of the large showers with energies up to $4 \cdot 10^{11}$ eV observed behind 12 cm. of lead. Since singly charged particles with energies above $60 \cdot 10^9$ eV can have no latitude effect, one must conclude that either the primary particles of these large showers are multiply charged (according to (17) and according to page 169 a field sensitivity of the intensity is not to be expected for n-fold charged particles for $r_{10} > 1$, or for energies greater than $n \cdot 60 \cdot 10^9$ eV), or that the energy of the shower is not the same as the energy of the primary particle but has its origin elsewhere (Vallarta (V 5)). Considering the fundamental significance of this conclusion, it would be desirable to have the latitude effect of the large showers very extensively and systematically investigated experimentally.

7. The Worldwide Fluctuations of Cosmic Ray Intensity

Worldwide fluctuations are those which extend over the whole surface of the earth. They are partly periodic and partly non-periodic. They may be distinguished as

1. Non-periodic fluctuations which correlate with the magnetic disturbances or magnetic storms.
2. Fluctuations with a period of the solar day.
3. Fluctuations with a period of 27 days.
4. Fluctuations with a period of one year.
5. Fluctuations with a period of one sidereal day.

For the magnetic disturbances ring currents in spatially closed unstable periodic orbits seem to play a rôle (Godart (G 7, 8); Störmer (S 20)).

For the fluctuations with the periods of one solar day, of 27 days, and of one year, one is tempted to assume a magnetic field of the sun as the cause. These fluctuations might take place as the position of the magnetic field of the sun with respect to the earth changes with the corresponding period. In particular, the period of 27 days should depend upon the rotation of the sun about its own axis. Almost no accurate information is available today about the magnetic field of the sun. The order of magnitude should be about 10 to 30 gauss at the sun's outer surface if one uses the Zeeman effect measurements of the solar spectrum of Hale, Seares, Maanen and Ellerman (H 17). However, this magnetic field seems to fall off very rapidly with elevation and it can be detected only up to a few hundred kilometers. It is, therefore, questionable whether one can count on magnetic effects at great distances. (cf. for example Handbuch der Astrophys. IV, Kap 2, p. 20).

Nevertheless, one can choose the simplest case as a working hypothesis, namely, a magnetic dipole of moment M_S. From the existence of a period of 27 days, one must conclude that the direction of this dipole does not coincide with the axis of rotation of the sun.

For the motion of charged particles one can count on the magnetic field of the earth as having a sphere of influence of about 250,000 km., beyond which the dipole field of the sun has the dominating effect. All considerations hold in regard to the dipole field of the sun as were invoked regarding the dipole field of the earth. However, an important simplification comes in because the space between the earth and the sun is empty and thus there can be no shadow effect in the dipole field of the sun for an observer on the earth. Hence, only the directions in the Störmer cone, which is associated with the dipole field of the sun, are forbidden by the solar magnetic field. In the first approximation one can add to the directions forbidden by the earth's field those forbidden by the Störmer cone of the solar field. In this way one gets the totality of the allowed and forbidden directions. In the second approximation one has to take account of the fact that the forbidden orbits with directions lying within the Störmer cone of the solar dipole are deflected in the sphere of influence of the earth. The deflection $\Delta\varphi$ is to be calculated by an integration of (15) over the sphere of influence.

The daily variations of the intensity of cosmic radiation depend then upon the daily rotation of the Störmer cone of the solar dipole with respect to a coordinate system fixed in the point of observation. The fluctuations with the period of 27 days depend upon the fluctuations of the heliomagnetic latitude of the earth and on the corresponding fluctuations of the Störmer cone of the solar dipole. The period of one year has various causes: One is the yearly fluctuation in the earth-sun distance; another is the yearly fluctuation of the heliomagnetic latitude of the earth in case the solar dipole is not perpendicular to the plane of the ecliptic; finally, as a third cause, there are the variations of geometric position of the Störmer cone of the solar dipole with respect to a given point of observation.

Carrying through the calculations of these fluctuations under the assumption that the magnetic field of the sun can be described by a dipole, Vallarta and Godart (V 9) obtained results in general qualitative agreement with the observed fluctuations. Certain larger deviations can perhaps be explained by the influence of the ionosphere and by temperature effects.

Janossy (J 1) was the first to suggest an important result from the assumption of a magnetic dipole field of the sun. Such a field would keep away from the earth all particles with energy under a certain minimum. If the orbit of the earth is not far from the heliomagnetic equator, then, according to Table 2, particles of energy below $r_{1s} = 0.414$ can not reach the earth. Here r_{1s} is to be evaluated from (17), where r_1 is the earth-sun distance and M is the magnetic moment of the solar dipole. Thus there could be no latitude effect in those latitudes in which primary particles with energies less than 0.414 are responsible for such an effect. Actually a latitude effect is present only between $+ 40°$ and $- 40°$ (cf. for example Gill (G 4)). According to Table 2, one can conclude from this that the particles reaching the earth must have an energy of at least 4 BeV, and if one substitutes this value for the energy, and $r_{1s} = 0.414$ in (17), there is obtained a magnetic dipole moment of the sun which yields a field strength at the surface of the sun of the order of magnitude of the observed value. However, for the disappearance of the latitude effect, there is another interpretation depending upon the fact that the low energy particles which could still be incident in high latitudes are unable to penetrate the entire atmosphere and in this way they fail to produce a latitude effect. The fact that the limit (the so-called knee) of the latitude effect is displaced to higher latitudes at great heights is also evidence favoring the latter interpretation.

The fluctuations in the intensity of cosmic radiation with the period of the sidereal day were interpreted by Compton and Getting (C 6) and by Vallarta, Graef and Kusaka (V 8) as a rotation of the galaxy and a motion of the earth resulting from it of about one thousandth the velocity of light. Another possibility for such fluctuations would be given by magnetic fields in the galactic system; in case the magnetic moments of the individual stars are randomly oriented such an effect is not to be expected according to Vallarta and Feynman (V 7).

REFERENCES TO THE LITERATURE

A 1   AGENO, M., G. BERNARDINI, B. N. CACCIAPUOTI, B. FERRETTI and G. C. WICK. Physic. Rev. **57**, 945 (1940).

A 2   ALEXEEVA, K. I.: C. r. Acad. Sci. URSS **26**, 28 (1940).

A 3   ANDERSON, C. D.: Physic. Rev. **44**, 406 (1933).

A 4   ANDERSON, C. D., and S. H. NEDDERMEYER: Physic. Rev. **50**, 263 (1936).

A 5   ARLEY, N.: Proc. roy. Soc. Lond. A **168**, 519 (1938).

A 6   ARLEY, N., and W. HEITLER: Nature (Lond.) **142**, 158 (1938).

A 7   AUGER, P.: Kernphysik. (Züricher Vorträge.) Hrsg. v. BRETSCHER. 1936.

A 8   AUGER, P., L. LEPRINCE RINGUET and P. EHRENFEST: J. Physique et Radium **7**, 58 (1936).

A 9   AUGER, P., R. MAZE and J. ROBLEY: C. r. Acad. Sci. Paris **208**, 1641 (1939).

A 10 AUGER, P., R. MAZE and T. GRIVET-MEYER: C. r. Acad. Sci. Paris **206**, 1721 (1938).

A 11 AUGER, P., R. MAZE, P. EHRENFEST and A. FRÉON: J. Physique et Radium **1**, 39 (1939).

A 12 AUGER, P., and A. ROSENBERG: C. r. Acad. Sci. Paris **201**, 1116 (1935).

B 1   BAGGÉ, E.: Ann. Physik **39**, 512 (1941).

B 1a BAGGÉ, E.: Ann. Phys. **39**, 535 (1941).

B 1b BAGGÉ, E.: Ann. Phys. **35**, 118 (1939).

B 2   BAÑOS, A.: J. Math. Physics **18**, 211 (1939).

B 3   BAÑOS, A.: J. Franklin Inst. **227**, 623 (1939).

B 4   BAÑOS, A.: Physic. Rev. **55**, 621 (1939).

B 5   BAÑOS, A., H. URIBE and J. LIFSHITZ: Rev. Modern Physics **11**, 137 (1939).

B 6   BARNÓTHY, J.: Z. Physik **115**, 140 (1940).

B 7   BELENKY, S.: C. r. Acad. Sci. URSS, N. s. **30**, 608 (1941).

B 8   BERNARDINI, G., B. N. CACCIAPUOTI and B. FERRETTI: Ric. Scient. **10**, 731 (1939).

B 9   BERNARDINI, G., B. N. CACCIAPUOTI, B. FERRETTI, O. PICCIONI and G. C. WICK: Physic. Rev. **58**, 1017 (1940).

B 10 BETHE, H.: Ann. Physik **5**, 325 (1930).

B 11 BETHE, H.: Handb. d. Physik **24**/1, 273 (1933).

B 12 BETHE, H. A.: Physic. Rev. **55**, 1130 (1938).

B 13 BETHE, H. A.: Physic. Rev. **57**, 260 (1940).

B 14 BETHE, H. A.: Physic. Rev. **57**, 390 (1940).

B 15 BETHE, H. A.: Physic. Rev. **59**, 684 (1941).

B 16 BETHE, H., and W. HEITLER: Proc. roy. Soc. Lond. **146**, 83 (1934).

B 17 BETHE, H. A., S. A. KORFF and G. PLACZEK: Physic. Rev. **57**, 573 (1940).

B 18 BETHE, H. A., and L. W. NORDHEIM: Physic. Rev. **57**, 998 (1940).

B 19 BHABHA, H. J.: Proc. roy. Soc. Lond. **164**, 257 (1937).

B 20 BHABHA, H. J.: Proc. roy. Soc. Lond. A **166**, 501 (1938).

B 21 BHABHA, H. J.: Nature (Lond.) **143**, 276 (1939).

B 22 BLACKETT, P. M. S.: Proc. roy. Soc. Lond. A **159**, 1 (1937).

B 23 BLACKETT, P. M. S.: Nature (Lond.) **142**, 992 (1938).

B 24 BLACKETT, P. M. S.: Proc. roy. Soc. Lond. **165**, 11 (1938).

B 25 BLAU, M., and H. WAMBACHER: Nature (Lond.) **140**, 585 (1937).
B 26 BLOCH, F.: Z. Physik **81**, 363 (1933).
B 27 BLOCH, F., and A. NORDSIECK: Physic. Rev. **52**, 54 (1937).
B 28 BOHR, N.: Philosophic. Mag. **25**, 10 (1913); **30**, 581 (1915).
B 29 BOOTH, F., and A. H. WILSON: Proc. roy. Soc. Lond. A **175**, 483 (1940).
B 30 BOPP, F.: In publication.
B 30a BOTHE, W.: Kernphysik, Zürich. Vorträge. 112 (1936).
B 31 BOUCKAERT, L.: Ann. Soc. Sci. Bruxelles A **54**, 174 (1934).
B 32 BOWEN, J. S., R. A. MILLIKAN and H. V. NEHER: Physic. Rev. **52**, 80 (1937).
B 33 BOWEN, J. S., R. A. MILLIKAN and H. V. NEHER: Physic. Rev. **53**, 217 (1938).
B 34 BOWEN, J. S., R. A. MILLIKAN and H. V. NEHER: Physic. Rev. **53**, 855 (1938).
B 35 BRADDICK, J. J., and G. S. HENSBY: Nature (Lond.) **144**, 1012 (1939).
C 1 CACCIAPUOTI, B. N.: Ric. Scient. **10**, 1082 (1939).
C 2 CERENKOV, P.: C. r. Acad. Sci. URSS **14**, 101 (1937).
C 3 CHRISTY, R. F., and S. KUSAKA: Physic. Rev. **59**, 414 (1941).
C 4 CLAY, J., and A. VAN GEMERT: Physica **6**, 497 (1939).
C 5 COCCONI, G., and V. TONGIORGI: Z. Physik **118**, 88 (1941).
C 5a COCCONI, G., A. LOVERDO and V. TONGIORGI: Naturwiss. **31**, 135 (1943).
C 6 COMPTON, A. H., and I. A. GETTING: Physic. Rev. **47**, 817 (1935).
C 7 COMPTON, A. H., and R. N. TURNER: Physic. Rev. **52**, 799 (1937).
C 8 COOPER, D. M.: Physic. Rev. **55**, 1272 (1939).
C 9 COOPER, D. M.: Physic. Rev. **57**, 68; **58**, 288 (1940).
C 10 CURRAN, S. C., and J. E. STROTHERS: Nature (Lond.) **145**, 224 (1940), Nr 3667— Proc. roy. Soc. Lond. A **172**, 72 (1939). Nr. 948.
D 1 DAUDIN, J.: Etudes sur les gerbes de rayons cosmiques. Paris 1942.
E 1 EHMERT, A.: Z. Physik **106**, 751 (1937).
E 2 EHMERT, A.: Z. Physik **115**, 326 (1940).
E 3 EULER, H.: Z. Physik **110**, 450, 692 (1938).
E 4 EULER, H.: Naturwiss. **26**, 382 (1938).
E 5 EULER, H.: Z. Physik **116**, 73 (1940).
E 6 EULER, H., and B. KOCKEL: Naturwiss. **23**, 246 (1935).
E 7 EULER, H., and W. HEISENBERG: Erg. exakt. Naturwiss. **17**, 1 (1938).
E 8 EULER, H., and H. WERGELAND: Astrophysica Norwegica **3**, 165 (1940).
F 1 FERMI, E.: Physic. Rev. **57**, 485 (1940).
F 2 FERMI, E., and B. ROSSI: Rend. R. Acad. Naz. Lincei **17**, 346 (1933).
F 3 FILIPPOV, A., I. GUREVICH and A. ZHDANOV (A. GDANOV): J. Physic. Sov.-Union **1**, 51 (1939).
F 4 FRÖHLICH, H., W. HEITLER and N. KEMMER: Proc. roy. Soc. Lond. **166**, 154 (1939).
F 5 FÜNFER, E.: Naturwiss. **25**, 235 (1937).
F 6 FÜNFER, E.: Z. Physik **111**, 351 (1938).
F 7 FUSSELL, L.: Physic. Rev. **51**, 1005 (1936).
G 1 GAMOW, G., and E. TELLER: Physic. Rev. **49**, 895 (1936).
G 2 GEIGER, H., and M. HEYDEN: Z. Physik **93**, 543 (1934).
G 3 GEIGER, H., and W. STUBBE: Abh. preuss. Akad. Wiss., **1941**, 3, No. 10.
G 4 GILL, P. A.: Physic. Rev. **55**, 1151 (1939).
G 5 GODART, O.: Ann. Soc. Sci. Bruxelles A **58**, 27 (1938).
G 6 GODART, O.: Physic. Rev. **55**, 875 (1939).
G 7 GODART, O.: Physic. Rev. **56**, 1074 (1939).
G 8 GODART, O.: J. Math. Physics **20**, 207 (1941).

G 9 GRIVET-MEYER, T.: C. r. Acad. Sci. Paris **206**, 833 (1938).
G 10 GRÖNBLOM, B. O.: Physic. Rev. **56**, 508 (1939).
G 11 GROSS, B.: Z. Physik **83**, 214 (1933).
H 1 HEISENBERG, W.: Z. Physik **101**, 533 (1936).
H 1a HEISENBERG, W.: Ber. Sächs. Akad.; Abh. math. phys. Kl. **89**, 369 (1937).
H 2 HEISENBERG, W.: Z. Physik **110**, 251 (1938).
H 3 HEISENBERG, W.: Z. Physik **113**, 61 (1939).
H 4 HEITLER, W.: Quantum-Theory of Radiation. Oxford: Clarendon-Press 1936.
H 5 HEITLER, W.: Proc. roy. Soc. Lond. **161**, 261 (1937).
H 6 HEITLER, W.: Proc. roy. Soc. Lond. A **166**, 529 (1938).
H 7 HERZOG, G.: Physic. Rev. **59**, 117 (1941).
H 8 HERZOG, G., and W. H. BOSTICK: Physic. Rev. **58**, 278 (1940).
H 9 HERZOG, G., and W. H. BOSTICK: Physic. Rev. **59**, 122 (1941).
H 10 HERZOG, G., and P. SCHERRER: Helvet. phys. Acta **8**, 514 (1935).
H 11 HESS, V. F.: Physik. Z. **14**, 610 (1913).
H 12 HOFFMANN, G., and W. S. PFORTE: Physik. Z. **31**, 347 (1930).
H 13 HUGHES, D. J.: Physic. Rev. **57**, 592 (1940).
H 14 HUTNER, R. A.: Physic. Rev. **55**, 15 (1939).
H 15 HUTNER, R. A.: Physic. Rev. **55**, 109 (1939).
H 16 HUTNER, R. A.: Physic. Rev. **55**, 614 (1939).
H 17 HALE, G. E., F. H. SEARES, A. v. MAANEN and F. ELLERMANN: J. Astrophys. **47**, 206 (1918).
J 1 JÁNOSSY, L.: Z. Physik **104**, 430 (1937).
J 2 JÁNOSSY, L.: Proc. roy. Soc. Lond. A **179**, 361 (1942).
J 3 JÁNOSSY, L., and P. INGLEBY: Nature (Lond.) **145**, 511 (1940); **147**, 56 (1941).
J 4 JÁNOSSY, L., and B. C. LOVELL: Nature (Lond.) **142**, 716 (1938).
J 5 JENSEN, H.: VERH. dtsch. physik. Ges. (3) **20**, 113 (1939).
J 6 JESSE, W. P., and P. S. GILL: Physic. Rev. **55**, 414 (1939).
J 7 JOHNSON, T. H.: Physic. Rev. **47**, 318 (1934).
J 8 JOHNSON, T. H.: Physic. Rev. **54**, 385 (1938).
J 9 JOHNSON, T. H.: Rev. Modern Physics **10**, 193 (1938).
J 10 JOHNSON, T. H.: Physic. Rev. **56**, 226 (1939).
J 11 JOHNSON, T. H.: J. Franklin Inst. **227**, 37 (1939).
J 12 JOHNSON, T. H.: Rev. Modern Physics **11**, 208 (1939).
J 13 JOHNSON, T. H., and J. G. BARRY: Physic. Rev. **56**, 219 (1939).
J 14 JONES, H.: Rev. Modern Physics **11**, 235 (1939).
J 15 JORDAN, B. G.: Erg. exakt. Naturwiss. **16**, 47 (1937).
J 16 JUILFS, J.: Naturwiss. (in publication).
K 1 KEMMER, N.: Proc. Cambridge philos. Soc. **34**, 354 (1938).
K 2 KOENIG, H. P.: Physic. Rev. **58**, 385 (1940).
K 3 KOLHÖRSTER, W.: Physik. Z. **14**, 1153 (1913).
K 4 KOLHÖRSTER, W., J. MATTHES and E. WEBER: Naturwiss. **26**, 576 (1938).
K 5 KOLHÖRSTER, W., and J. MATTHES: Physik. Z. **40**, 142, 617 (1939).
K 6 KORFF, S. A.: Physic. Rev. **56**, 210 (1939)—Rev. Modern Physics **11**, 211 (1939).
K 6a KULENKAMPFF, H.: Verh. dtsch. phys. Ges. (3), **19**, 92 (1938).
K 7 KUNZE, P.: Z. Physik **80**, 559 (1933).
K 8 KUNZE, P.: Z. Physik **83**, 1 (1939).
L 1 LANDAU, L.: J. of Physics **3**, 237 (1940).
L 2 LANDAU, L., and G. RUMER: Proc. roy. Soc. Lond. **166**, 213 (1938).
L 3 LEISEGANG, S.: Z. Physik **116**, 515 (1940).

L 4 LEMAÎTRE, G.: Ann. Soc. Sci. Bruxelles A **54**, 162 and 194 (1934).
L 5 LEMAÎTRE, G.: Nature (Lond.) **140**, 23 (1937).
L 6 LEMAÎTRE, G., and M. S. VALLARTA: Physic. Rev. **43**, 87 (1933).
L 7 LEMAÎTRE, G., and M. S. VALLARTA: Ann. Soc. Sci. Bruxelles A **56**, 102 (1936).
L 8 LEMAÎTRE, G., and M. S. VALLARTA: Physic. Rev. **49**, 719 (1936).
L 9 LEMAÎTRE, G., and M. S. VALLARTA: Physic. Rev. **50**, 493 (1936).
L 10 LEMAÎTRE, G., M. S. VALLARTA and L. BOUCKAERT: Physic. Rev. **47**, 434 (1935).
L 11 LEPRINCE-RINGUET, L., S. GORODETZKY, E. NAGEOTTE and R. RICHARD-FOY: CR **211**, 382 (1940).
L 12 LYONS, D.: Physik. Z. **42**, 166 (1941).
M 1 MAASS, H.: Physik. Z. **35**, 858 (1934).
M 2 MAASS, H.: Ann. Physik (5) **27**, 507 (1936).
M 3 MATTAUCH, J., and S. FLÜGGE: Kernphysikal. Tabellen. Berlin: Springer 1942.
M 3a MIEHLNICKEL, E.: Höhenstrahlung 1933.
M 4 MOLIÈRE, G.: Naturwiss. **30**, 87 (1942); complete article to be published in Z. Physik.
M 5 MÖLLER, CHR., and L. ROSENFELD: Danske Vid. Selsk., Math. Fys. Medd. **17**, 8 (1940).
M 6 MONTGOMERY, C. G., and D. D. MONTGOMERY: Rev. Modern Physics **11**, 255 (1939).
N 2 NEDDERMEYER, S. H., and C. D. ANDERSON: Rev. Modern Physics **11**, 191 (1939).
N 3 NIE, H.: Z. Physik **99**, 453 and 776 (1936).
N 4 NIELSEN, W. M., and K. Z. MORGAN: Physic. Rev. **54**, 245 (1938).
N 5 NIELSEN, W. M., C. M. RYERSON, L. W. NORDHEIM and K. Z. MORGAN: Physic. Rev. **57**, 158 (1940).
N 6 NIELSEN, W. M., C. M. RYERSON, L. W. NORDHEIM and K. Z. MORGAN: Physic. Rev. **59**, 547 (1941).
N 7 NORDHEIM, L. W.: Physic. Rev. **53**, 694 (1938).
N 8 NORDHEIM, L. W.: Physic. Rev. **56**, 502 (1939).
N 9 NORDHEIM, L. W., and M. H. HEBB: Physic. Rev. **56**, 494 (1939).
N 10 NORDSIECK, A.: Physic. Rev. **52**, 59 (1937).
O 1 OPPENHEIMER, J. R.: Rev. Modern Physics **11**, 264 (1939).
O 2 OPPENHEIMER, J. R., H. SNYDER and R. SERBER: Physic. Rev. **57**, 75 (1940).
P 1 PAULI, W., and W. WEISSKOPF: Helvet. phys. Acta **7**, 709 (1934).
P 2 PFOTZER, G.: Z. Physik **102**, 23 (1936).
P 3 PFOTZER, G.: Z. Physik **102**, 41 (1936).
P 4 POMERANTZ, M. A.: Physic. Rev. **57**, 3 (1940).
P 5 POMERANTZ, M. A., and T. H. JOHNSON: Physic. Rev. **55**, 104, 600, 1112 (1939).
P 6 POWELL, W. M.: Physic. Rev. **60**, 413 (1941).
P 7 PROCA, J.: J. of Physics A **7**, 347 (1936).
P 8 PRIMAKOFF, H., and T. HOLSTEIN: Phys. Rev. **55**, 1218 (1939).
R 1 RASETTI, F.: Physic. Rev. **60**, 198 (1941).
R 2 REGENER, E., and A. EHMERT: Z. Physik **111**, 501 (1939).
R 3 RIBNER, H. S.: Physic. Rev. **55**, 1271 (1939).
R 4 RIBNER, H. S.: Physic. Rev. **56**, 1069 (1939).
R 5 ROSSI, B.: Nature (Lond.) **132**, 173 (1933).
R 6 ROSSI, B.: Rev. Modern Physics **11**, 296 (1939).
R 7 ROSSI, B., and D. B. HALL: Physic. Rev. **59**, 223 (1941).
R 8 ROSSI, B., N. HILBERRY and J. B. HOAG: Physic. Rev. **56**, 837 (1939).

R 9 Rossi, B., N. Hilberry and J. B. Hoag: Physic. Rev. **57**, 461 (1940).
R 10 Rossi, B., and V. H. Regener: Physic. Rev. **58**, 837 (1940).
R 11 Rozental, S.: Physic. Rev. **60**, 612 (1941).
R 12 Rumbaugh, G. H., and G. L. Locher: Physic. Rev. **49**, 855 (1936).
S 1 Santagelo, M., and E. Scrocco: Ric. Scient. **11**, 601 (1940).
S 1a Sauter, F.: Ann. d. Phys. (5) **18**, 486 (1933); **20**, 404 (1934).
S 2 Schein, M., and P. S. Gill: Rev. Modern Physics **11**, 267 (1939).
S 3 Schein, M., and P. S. Gill: Physic. Rev. **55**, 1111 (1939).
S 4 Schein, M., W. P. Jesse and E. O. Wollan: Physic. Rev. **57**, 847 (1940).
S 5 Schein, M., W. P. Jesse and E. O. Wollan: Physic. Rev. **59**, 615 (1941).
S 6 Schein, M., W. P. Jesse and E. O. Wollan: Physic. Rev. **59**, 930 (1941).
S 7 Schein, M., and V. C. Wilson: Rev. Modern Physics **11**, 292 (1939).
S 8 Schein, M., E. O. Wollan and G. Groetzinger: Physic. Rev. **58**, 1027 (1940).
S 9 Schmeiser, K., and W. Bothe: Ann. Physik **32**, 161 (1938)—Schmeiser, K.: Z. Physik **112**, 501 (1939).
S 10 Schönberg, M.: Ann. Acad. Brasil. Sci. **12**, 281 (1940).
S 11 Schopper, E.: Naturwiss. **25**, 557 (1937).
S 12 Schopper, E. M., and E. Schopper: Physik. Z. **40**, 22 (1939).
S 13 Schremp, E. J.: Physic. Rev. **54**, 153 (1938).
S 14 Schremp, E. J.: Physic. Rev. **54**, 158 (1939).
S 15 Schremp, E. J.: Physic. Rev. **57**, 1061 (1940).
S 16 Schremp, E. J.: and H. S. Ribner: Rev. Modern Physics **11**, 149 (1939).
S 17 Siegert, B.: Z. Physik **118**, 217 (1941).
S 18 Sittkus, A.: Z. Physik **112**, 626 (1939).
S 18a Steinke, E. G.: Ergebn. exakt. Naturwiss. **13**, 89 (1934).
S 18b Steinmaurer, R.: Ergebn. d. kosm. Physik **3**, 38 (1938).
S 19 Stetter, G., and H. Wambacher: Physik. Z. **40**, 702 (1939).
S 20 Störmer, C.: Z. Astrophys. **1**, 237 (1930).
S 21 Störmer, C.: Univ. Publ. Univ. Obs. Oslo **1934**, No. 10, No. 12—Astrophysica Norvegica **1**, 115 (1936); **2**, 193 (1937).
S 22 Street, J. C., and R. H. Woodward: Physic. Rev. **49**, 198 (1936).
S 23 Stuhlinger, E.: Z. Physik **116**, 281 (1939).
S 24 Swann, W. F. G.: Physic. Rev. **44**, 224 (1933).
S 25 Swann, W. F. G.: Physic. Rev. **44**, 124 (1933).
S 26 Swann, W. F. G.: Rev. Modern Physics **11**, 251 (1939).
S 27 Swann, W. F. G.: Physic. Rev. **59**, 770 (1941); **58**, 200 (1940).
S 28 Swann, W. F. G.: Physic. Rev. **60**, 470 (1941).
T 1 Takeuchi, T., T. Inai, T. Sugita and M. Huzisawa: Proc. Phys.-Math. Soc. Jap. **19**, 88 (1937).
T 2 Tomonaga, S., and G. Araki: Physic. Rev. **58**, 90 (1940).
V 1 Vallarta, M. S.: Physic. Rev. **44**, 1 (1933).
V 2 Vallarta, M. S.: Physic. Rev. **47**, 647 (1935).
V 3 Vallarta, M. S.: Nature (Lond.) **139**, 24 (1937).
V 4 Vallarta, M. S.: Rev. Modern Physics **11**, 239 (1939).
V 5 Vallarta, M. S.: Physic. Rev. **55**, 583 (1939).
V 6 Vallarta, M. S.: J. Franklin Inst. **227**, 1 (1939).
V 7 Vallarta, M. S., and R. P. Feynman: Physic. Rev. **55**, 506 (1939).
V 8 Vallarta, M. S., C. Graef and S. Kusaka: Physic. Rev. **55**, 1 (1939).
V 9 Vallarta, M. S., and O. Godart: Rev. Modern Physics **11**, 180 (1939).
W 1 Wambacher, H.: Wiener Ber. **149**, 157 (1940).

W 2 WATAGHIN, G., M. D. SANTOS and P. H. POMPEJA: Physic. Rev. **57**, 61 (1940).
W 3 WEISZ, P.: Physic. Rev. **59**, 845 (1941).
W 4 WENTZEL, G.: Naturwiss. **26**, 273 (1938).
W 5 WENTZEL, G.: Helvet. phys. Acta **13**, 269 (1940).
W 6 WICK, G. C.: Unpublished communication to W. HEISENBERG.
W 7 WIDHALM, A.: Z. Physik **115**, 481 (1940).
W 8 WIGNER, E. P., C. L. CRITCHFIELD and E. TELLER: Physic. Rev. **56**, 530 (1939).
W 9 WILLIAMS, E. J.: Proc. roy. Soc. Lond. A **169**, 531 (1939).
W 10 WILLIAMS, E. J.: Proc. roy. Soc. Lond. **172**, 194 (1939).
W 11 WILLIAMS, E. J., and G. R. EVANS: Nature (Lond.) **145**, 818 (1940).
W 12 WILLIAMS, E. J., and G. E. ROBERTS: Nature (Lond.) **145**, 102 (1940).
W 13 WILSON, V. C.: Physic. Rev. **53**, 337 (1938).
W 14 WILSON, V. C.: Physic. Rev. **55**, 6 (1939).
W 15 WILSON, J. G.: Proc. roy. Soc. Lond. A **172**, 517 (1939).
W 16 WOLLAN, E.: Physic. Rev. **60**, 532 (1941).
Y 1 YONG-LI, TSCHANG: Ann. Soc. Sci. Bruxelles A **59**, 285 (1939).
Y 2 YUKAWA, H.: Proc. Phys.-Math. Soc. Jap. **17**, 48 (1935).
Y 3 YUKAWA, H.: Proc. Phys.-Math. Soc. Jap. **19**, 712 (1937).
Y 4 YUKAWA, H., and S. SAKATA: Proc. Phys.-Math. Soc. Jap. **19**, 1084 (1937).
Y 5 YUKAWA, H., M. TAKETANI and S. SAKATA: Proc. Phys.-Math. Soc. Jap. **20**, 319 (1938).
Y 6 YUKAWA, H., S. SAKATA, M. KOBAYASI and M. TAKETANI: Proc. Phys.-Math. Soc. Jap. **20**, 720 (1938).

INDEX